Women of Grace®

Full of Grace

WOMEN AND THE ABUNDANT LIFE

The Women of Grace® Foundational Study Series

JOHNNETTE S. BENKOVIC, et al.

SIMON PETER PRESS

NIHIL OBSTAT:
Reverend David J. Davis
Censor Deputatus

IMPRIMATUR:
Most Reverend Fabian W. Bruskewitz, D.D., S.T.D.
Bishop of Lincoln
March 10, 2005

The *NIHIL OBSTAT* and *IMPRIMATUR* are official declarations that a book or a pamphlet is free from doctrinal or moral error. No implication is contained therein that those who have granted the *NIHIL OBSTAT* and *IMPRIMATUR* agree with the contents, opinions or statements expressed.

Published by Simon Peter Press, Inc. PO Box 2187, Oldsmar, FL 34677

05 06 07 08 09 10 9 8 7 6 5 4 3 2 1

Printed in the United States of America

ISBN: 0-9761533-5-1

Library of Congress Cataloging-in-Publication Data
Benkovic, Johnnette S.
Full of grace: women and the abundant life study guide/Johnnette S. Benkovic
Includes bibliographical references.
ISBN 0-9761533-5-1
1. Women/Roman Catholic 2. Bible Studies I. Title

Table of Contents

A Word from Johnnette S. Benkovic

My Dear Sister in Christ,

Welcome to the Women of Grace® Foundational Study Series, *Full of Grace: Women and the Abundant Life!* You are about to embark upon a transforming journey as you explore the great call and gift of your femininity. Along the way, you will meet some of the great women saints, learn from the wisdom and guidance of Holy Mother Church, and begin to unpack the treasures of Sacred Scripture. By looking to the Blessed Virgin Mary who is our exemplar, you will find a spiritual path that leads you to the heart of the Father and the abundant life of Jesus Christ. Most importantly, you will discover your great dignity and vocation as a daughter of God and the *feminine genius* that is yours by virtue of your gender.

In addition, you will:

- Uncover the "secret" to personal fulfillment and hope.
- Deepen your appreciation and understanding of the Catholic faith, the Holy Mass and the Sacraments of Baptism, Reconciliation, and Eucharist.
- Learn what it takes to be a true friend.
- Discover the role our emotions play in our relationship with God and others.
- Recognize the strength of prayer, the power of obedience, and the light of true wisdom.
- Experience the healing power of the Holy Spirit.
- Find out why women are God's "special agents" in this new millennium.
- Be equipped to fulfill your call and mission as a woman of grace in the world today.

This is an important time for woman. Throughout his pontificate, Pope John Paul II has written extensively on the dignity, nature and role of woman in the plan of God, and has exhorted her to come to a deeper experience of her essential nature and spirit which he calls the *genius of woman* or the *feminine genius*. He has encouraged the women of the world to accept and develop the gift of their authentic femininity as the means and source through which they can experience happiness and hope, initiate and sustain cultural change, instill true and lasting peace in interpersonal relationships, and promote justice and freedom, truth and love in the world and the culture of the day. He offers them the example of the Blessed Virgin Mary as their model and guide, and tells them, "the time has come to move from words to deeds."

Indeed, woman's gifts and talents are essential for the world today. Her innate understanding of the human person, her compassion for the poor and weak, her intuitive ability to get to the heart of a situation, her patience and capacity to persevere, her generosity of heart, her inner strength and fortitude are all desperately needed in today's culture. Our hope is that by the end of this study, you have discovered all of these gifts, and so many more, within your own heart and spirit. God is looking to you to be a conduit of His love and mercy to the world today!

Please be assured of my prayers for you as you participate in this Women of Grace® Foundational Study Series. I am asking the Father to bestow upon you every spiritual blessing in the heavens (Ephesians 1:3). May God bless you, and may the abundant life of Jesus Christ be yours!

Your Sister in Christ,

Johnnette S Benkovic

Acknowledgments

The development of this foundational study series for *Women of Grace*® has been a labor of love, patience, and effort on the part of many people. Its broad appeal is largely due to the "voice" it has been given by all of the special ladies whose contributions comprise it: Mary Jo Anderson, Ronda Chervin, Genevieve Kineke, Rosalind Moss, Dale O'Leary, and Heidi Hess Saxton. Thank you for sharing in the process and helping to make this study series a reality.

Thank you to Christine Andersen, a young mother who contacted me about how she was using my book, *Full of Grace: Women and the Abundant Life*, in her women's group — you confirmed for me that what I was hearing in my heart was the way to go.

Thank you to Mary Harris who has been a valuable assistant in the *Women of Grace*® movement as well as an excellent sounding board and advisor for this foundational study. I have truly appreciated your help and encouragement, Mary.

Thank you to Father Edmund Sylvia, C.S.C., who patiently reviewed each lesson as I completed it, made thoughtful suggestions, and gave me new insights to consider, and turned everything around for me in record time! I am grateful, Father.

Thank you to Steven Motyl for the production of the videotape lessons. I appreciate your time and effort, Steve. Thank you also to Tom Sullivan for the "behind-the-scenes" work of making the lessons available to our focus group via Internet. And, thank you to our focus group. Your suggestions were helpful indeed!

Thank you to all of the staff members of Living His Life Abundantly® International, Inc: Jean Sutton, Joanne Kane, Jane Spencer, Thea Benkovic, Julie Rodriguez, Jo Welch, Nora Hunt, Ed Seepersad. Your help and prayers have been such a blessing.

A special thank you to the Most Reverend Fabian Bruskewitz, Diocese of Lincoln, for reviewing the Women of Grace® Foundational Study Series and giving it your Imprimatur. I am so grateful for your service to our apostolate, Your Excellency. And thank you to Reverend David J. Davis, Censor Deputatus, for your careful read and helpful suggestions.

Finally, thank you to my husband, Anthony, for your patience while this project was being developed and brought to completion. As always, your love, understanding, and tremendous support are the backbone of my efforts.

—JOHNNETTE S. BENKOVIC

Meet the Contributors

MARY JO ANDERSON — Catholic journalist and commentator. Mary Jo is a contributing editor to *Crisis Magazine* and served as editor-in-chief of this series. She brings a Catholic perspective to the global issues of our day and time, as well as their impact on women in the world today. Mary Jo serves on the Advisory Board for Women of Grace® and is a frequent guest on *The Abundant Life Television Program* (EWTN) and "Women of Grace® Live" (Catholic radio). Mary Jo is a popular conference speaker. She is a mother and grandmother and has been married to her husband, Frank, since 1966.

JOHNNETTE BENKOVIC — Founder and president of Women of Grace®, and founder and president of Living His Life Abundantly®. Johnnette has been active in the field of Catholic communications since 1987. She is host of *The Abundant Life Television Program* (EWTN) and "Women of Grace® Live" (Catholic radio). Author of several books, including *Full of Grace: Women and the Abundant Life*, Johnnette is a popular conference speaker and retreat facilitator. She is a mother and a grandmother, and has been married to her husband, Anthony, since 1973.

RONDA CHERVIN — Professor and writer. Ronda received her doctorate in philosophy from Fordham University and a masters in religious studies from Notre Dame Apostolic Institute. Ronda is a convert to Catholicism from Judaism. A prolific writer, Ronda is the author of some 50 books to date including *Feminine, Free and Faithful, Treasury of Women Saints, Prayers of the Women Mystics, Living In Love: About Christian Ethics,* and *A Mother's Treasury of Prayer.* She is an international speaker, a widow, a mother and a grandmother.

GENEVIEVE KINEKE — Founder of *Canticle Magazine* (formerly called Hearth) in 1992, Advisory Board Member of Women of Grace®, conference presenter and host of *Women in the Church Today*, a television and radio program. In 2003, Genevieve gave *Canticle* to Women of Grace® continuing on as a regularly featured contributor. She has been married to her husband, Charley, since 1984 and is the mother of five children.

ROSALIND MOSS — Apologist, conference presenter, television host. Born and raised in a Jewish home, Rosalind came to Catholicism by way of Evangelical Protestantism. She entered the Catholic Church at Easter 1995 after a long and arduous search for the Church Jesus founded. Rosalind is a staff apologist at Catholic Answers, and serves on the Advisory Board of Women of Grace®. She is a well-known conference speaker and co-hosts the television series, *Household of Faith* (EWTN).

DALE O'LEARY — Freelance writer and international advocate for women. Dale attended the Cairo Conference on Population and Development in Egypt in 1994, and the Beijing Conference on Women in China in 1995, both sponsored by the United Nations. There, she upheld the Catholic understanding of woman and worked diligently against the anti-life/anti-family agenda. Her experiences led her to write her book, *The Gender Agenda: Redefining Equality*. A frequent write for *Canticle Magazine*, Dale has been married to her husband, Terry, since 1963 and is mother to four children and grandmother to ten.

HEIDI HESS SAXTON — Editor — Heidi converted to the Catholic Church in 1994 and is a graduate student of theology at Sacred Heart Major Seminary in Detroit. She is a freelance journalist and author of the books *With Mary in Prayer: Meditations and Guidance from the Life of Mary, Let Nothing Trouble You: 60 Reflections from the Writings of Teresa of Avila,* and *Touched by Kindness: True Stories of People Blessed by Compassion.* She and her husband, Craig, are in the process of adopting their two foster children.

Introduction

The Women of Grace® Foundational Study Series is part of the Women of Grace® ministry to women. Women of Grace® is an outreach of Living His Life Abundantly® International, Inc. In his Letter to Women, Pope John Paul II writes, "...I am convinced that the secret of making speedy progress in achieving full respect for women and their identity...must first and foremost be won through an effective and intelligent campaign for the promotion of women, concentrating on all areas of woman's life and beginning with a universal recognition of the dignity of woman.

It is to this end that Women of Grace® has been founded. Its mission is to affirm women in their dignity and vocation as daughters of God and in their gift of authentic femininity by exploring all aspects of the feminine person including her spirituality, psychology, emotional reality, and physical being. Through an effective and intelligent campaign, Women of Grace® promotes the dignity of woman, the grace of true womanhood, and woman's fundamental call and mission in the world.

Women of Grace® conferences, retreats, study series, study groups, interactive website (www.womenofgrace.com), radio program, and *Canticle Magazine: The Voice of Women of Grace* comprise the multi-faceted strategy implemented to achieve its mission. A membership opportunity also exists for those women who are seeking a closer affiliation with each other and with the apostolate. Women participants are encouraged to become part of a "grassroots" *Women of Grace®* effort in their own parishes, communities, and geographic regions.

Women of Grace® does not seek to supplant the good work already being accomplished by other existing apostolates, but rather to supplement their efforts by providing them with materials and resources to aid them in accomplishing their own vision and mission. Therefore, *Women of Grace®* works to cooperate with the many faithful Catholic apostolates (particularly those for women) already organized throughout the United States and beyond.

HOW THIS STUDY SERIES WORKS

The primary objective of the Women of Grace® Foundational Study Series is to explore with you an authentic understanding of the gift of your femininity, and to help equip you to bring the grace of your gender to bear upon your interior being, your relationship with God, your interpersonal relationships, and the culture of the day. The feminine person will be studied in conjunction with Church teaching and Sacred Scripture specific to the dignity and value of womanhood. The Blessed Virgin Mary is our exemplar and model. Her strength, courage, and maternal love is our inspiration and hope.

MATERIALS:

In addition to this study guide, you will need three other items:

Full of Grace: Women and the Abundant Life by Johnnette S. Benkovic
Catechism of the Catholic Church
Holy Bible
(The study series quotes from Revised Standard Version, Catholic Edition, but you may use any translation.)

Note: If purchasing the above items is a hardship, both the Holy Bible and the *Catechism of the Catholic Church* are available on line. Most libraries are now equipped with computers that can be used free of charge.

For the Catechism and the Holy Bible go to:
www.womenofgrace.com/study

All materials are available for purchase by going to:
www.womenofgrace.com
Or calling:
800-558-5452

Or by writing to:
Women of Grace®
c/o Living His Life Abundantly® International, Inc.
325 Scarlet Blvd,
Oldsmar, FL 34677

THE STUDY GROUP:

The Women of Grace® Foundational Study Series uses a multi-media approach. Each week you will gather together with your study group to discuss the five lessons you have completed at home, view the weekly videotape lesson presented by Johnnette Benkovic, complete the Media Response Sheet while you view it, and discuss the answers you have recorded with your group.

In the group discussions, courtesy and affirming listening is the key. This means implementing some basic rules of etiquette (paying attention, not interrupting or talking out of turn, limiting your responses so everyone has a chance to share, not taking "center stage," etc.) and being totally present to the person speaking. The group meeting is not a time of problem-solving, or for emotional or spiritual counseling. It is also not a gripe session. Rather, it is a time to discover how the Holy Spirit is mightily present in each woman's life. The members of the group must be receptive listeners who seek to "hear" the action of the Holy Spirit at work in the lives of their sister members.

An open and respectful attitude must be maintained toward all of the women in your group. In addition, each woman's privacy and confidentiality must be respected. Gossip or "tale-carrying" finds no home in the *Women of Grace®* setting. The study group provides an opportunity for every woman to grow in the virtues of patience, cheerfulness, humility, and charity.

THE "AT HOME" LESSONS:

Each week you will complete five lessons at home. You will notice that each week of study has a special theme and corresponding grace to pray for. Before beginning each lesson, review the theme and the grace and ask God to help you mine the rich treasure of each. Every lesson includes an opening and closing prayer, questions for you to answer from the book, *Full of Grace: Women and the Abundant Life*, a section entitled *Know the Faith*, a Catholic "vocabulary word," *For Pondering* which features a contribution by another writer, and a "word of wisdom" leading to a closing prayer. In addition, each week you will read about two great women saints whose lives inspire us and instruct us in authentic femininity.

Many of the questions following each section are meant to encourage you to "dig deeply." St. Teresa of Avila once said there is no spiritual growth without self-knowledge. Do not be afraid to "go to the depths." Jesus is waiting for you there. Except for the questions that are directly related to the text, Sacred Scripture, or the teachings of the Church, there are no "right" or "wrong" answers. This is YOUR study — approach it as such. In some cases, the space provided for you in your study guide may not be sufficient for your response. For this reason, you may consider keeping a separate journal for your responses.

WHAT IS EXPECTED OF YOU:

You have invested in this study series by purchasing the study guide and the text. In addition, you may have purchased a copy of the *Catechism of the Catholic Church* and a bible. The very fact that you have sensed a desire to participate is an indication of the Holy Spirit's movement in you. Therefore:

- Plan on attending every meeting and completing the five lessons at home each week. While there is no question that duties, responsibilities, or unexpected circumstances can interfere with your commitment, it is important to discern between them and a tendency to look for an excuse to "opt out."
- If you must miss a study group meeting, contact your facilitator ahead of time if at all possible. In this way, the group will know to proceed without you. Also, arrange a time with your facilitator to find out when you can view the videotape presentation you will be missing, go over the lessons you have completed, and review any announcements or discussion points your group will have made in the meeting.
- It is an act of courtesy and charity to be prompt. Unavoidable situations can sometimes delay us. Again, make sure the delay is prompted by circumstances rather than procrastination. God cannot be outdone in generosity — give Him some time and He will give you more than you ever expected!

BECOME A MEMBER:

Many women have enjoyed a closer affiliation with each other and the *Women of Grace*® apostolate through membership. While all of the outreaches of *Women of Grace*® are available to everyone, there are some special benefits that apply to members. They are:

- 20% discount on all *Women of Grace*® products and merchandise
- Access to the "Members Only" section on the *Women of Grace*® website
- Special conference discounts
- VIP pre-conference reception to meet the speakers
- An annual subscription to *Canticle Magazine: The Voice of Women of Grace*
- Monthly Mass celebrated especially for the intentions of *Women of Grace*® members
- Free gift and membership card

Use the "Become a Member Form" in the Resource Section of your study guide, speak to your facilitator about becoming a member, join on-line at www.womenofgrace.com, or call 800-558-5452.

BECOME A FACILITATOR:

Is God asking you to share the *Women of Grace*® study group experience with other women by becoming a facilitator? If so, go to www.womenofgrace.com or call 800-558-5452 to find out how.

Chapter One

The Special Call and Gift of Woman

Full of Grace: This week covers pages 9-25 of the text.

Our first week together is filled with a holy mystery: How a woman, in the midst of "ordinary" duties, is invited to live out an extraordinary vocation that is uniquely her own, by virtue of her womanhood. She possesses feminine gifts that are vital to the modern world. Yet, too many of us worry that we can do nothing to make a difference, "What can I do? I am just one person!"

The answer is in the pages that follow, especially in the example of great women of the Bible and women saints throughout the history of the Church. Through them you will discover what you have "known but forgotten": that God has a particular plan for your life. There is not a day to waste. Each of us is needed at this critical moment in human history. If we respond in obedience to God's call, just imagine what God can do with us!

This first week we will consider the special call and mission of women, created to bring the life of Christ to the world. We do this, as Mary did, by remaining receptive to the Spirit, trusting and submissive to the perfect will of God as revealed through Jesus Christ. As we do this, we will bring the life and love of Christ to a world that is desperately seeking for truth. Let us consider, then, how we are to accomplish this important task:

LESSON ONE — Called by God
LESSON TWO — The Time for Woman is Now
LESSON THREE — The Influence of Woman's Vocation
LESSON FOUR — Impregnated with the Spirit of the Gospel
LESSON FIVE — Called to Radiate the Life of Christ

Questions To Ponder This Week

- Throughout Church history "ordinary" women have lived extraordinary lives, filled with the Holy Spirit. Why were women such as St. Gianna and St. Catherine of Genoa so influential, each in her own way?
- What women have made a difference in my life? How? Whose life has been (or will be) influenced by mine? Why? How?
- The Blessed Virgin's "*Fiat*" ("Let it be done unto me…") sets an example for us all: How have I responded to the grace of God? Give a specific example, complete with time and place.

Media Response Sheet

The Special Call and Gift of Woman

WEEKLY THEME:
God has created me for a special and unique purpose according to my feminine vocation.

WEEKLY GRACE:
I pray for the grace to recognize my call and mission and its relationship to my femininity.

Answer the following questions as you watch the pre-recorded lesson given by Johnnette S. Benkovic, founder of Women of Grace®.

1. What can we be assured of experiencing during the course of this study if we are faithful to our prayer time, do the lessons in the curriculum, and participate in the group meetings?

 ____

 ____

2. What passage from Sacred Scripture tells us who we are, why we are, and what our purpose and mission is in life? ____________________

3. Who are we? ____________________

 Why are we? ____________________

 What is our purpose and mission? ____________________

4. What are the three attributes of God and what do they mean?

 ________________ means ________________

 ________________ means ________________

 ________________ means ________________

 What do they tell us about our selection by God to be women? ________________

 ____

5. Why did God create us to be women?

 a. ______________________________________

 b. ______________________________________

6. What special gift of woman is specific to her? ______________________________

____

____

____

____

7. Everything about the feminine person signifies the reality that it is to woman that.... ______________

____

____

8. Our femininity is as inherent to our ______________ as it is to our ______________.

9. This means that all women, regardless of their state in life or physical capacity to bear life, are called to be ______

____.

10. Who is the perfection of the feminine vocation to be mother, and where do we see this in Sacred Scripture?

____

____

____

____

11. What are the three marks of a spiritual mother?

a. ____

b. ____

c. ____

12. As women, what is our call and mission at this moment in the history of man? Why is it so important?

____

____

____

____

____

Woman of Grace

St. Teresa Benedicta of the Cross (Edith Stein, 1891 – 1942)

She was a brilliant scholar, a contemplative mystic, and a "liberated" feminist. At various times she was also a devout Jew, an atheist, a philosopher, a Catholic, and a Carmelite nun. Hers was a heart that hungered for truth, with a passion that burned with such purity and clarity that Pope John Paul II, whose own *Mulieris Dignitatem* and "Letter to Women" bear the unmistakable imprint of her spirit, canonized her less than fifty years after her death at Auschwitz.

Edith Stein was born to a devout Jewish family in Breslaw (now Wroclaw, Poland) on Yom Kippur, the Jewish Day of Atonement. She lost her father when she was only two years old. Sustained by her faith, Edith's mother worked hard to support her eleven children. And yet, by the time she was a teenager, Edith no longer practiced her childhood faith. She considered herself an atheist.

Despite this, her search for truth continued. Edith was introduced to Christianity at university through her study of philosophy, which encouraged her to be open to "transcendent realities," as well as the example of friends who had converted to the faith. There were other signs as well: One day Edith observed a woman laden with packages, who entered the church and paused for a few moments' prayer. Edith was struck by the casual familiarity of that anonymous soul, who had stopped by for an "intimate chat" with God, a few moments of simple communion. She never saw the woman again, but her wordless example spoke volumes to Edith's hungry heart. Years later, Edith came upon the autobiography of Teresa of Avila, and read it in a single afternoon. So profoundly was she affected by it, Edith determined then and there to become both a Catholic and a Carmelite. (Although she did convert almost immediately, she did not take the habit of Carmel for another decade.)

After her conversion to the faith, Edith continued to write and lecture, and was a powerful voice in the Catholic Women's Movement in Germany from 1927 to 1933, until it was no longer safe for her to continue her work. She then entered the Carmel of Cologne just before her forty-second birthday. She spent five years there; her sister Rosa, who converted in 1936, worked at the convent as a third-order Carmelite.

By 1938 the convent walls could no longer protect the sisters, who were sent to Holland. Then the Netherlands fell under Hitler's power; not long after, the Dutch bishops wrote an encyclical denouncing the atrocities inflicted by the Nazis. All Roman Catholic Jews in Holland were rounded up for execution. Edith and Rosa were among those captured and sent to Auschwitz. Even in her last days on earth, Edith was a living witness to the power of the cross. As the Holocaust raged all around her, she saw the cross that had been placed upon on the shoulders of the Jewish people. "Most of them will not understand it," she wrote. "But those who do understand must accept it willingly in the name of all. I wanted to do that.... But in what the bearing of the cross was to consist I did not yet know."

A week after arriving at the camp, Edith and Rosa were both sent to the gas chambers. Edith was just fifty years old.

The role and nature of woman was the subject of Edith's most remarkable and original work. Unlike radical feminists of her time (and ours), Edith recognized the real, fundamental differences between the sexes. She believed that these differences are not arbitrary, but are imprinted upon us, body and soul. She insisted that these differences are not hierarchical or diminishing; rather, she perceived the complementarity of the sexes as a necessary good. Whether at home, in the workplace or professional environment, women have the power to transform society in ways that men cannot. And all is accomplished through the power of love, and the power of the cross.

FAITH IN ACTION

"Avoid truth without love, love without truth." In what ways did Edith Stein embody this truth? In what ways is God calling me to stand against these cultural evils?

Woman of Grace

St. Madeleine Sophie Barat (1779-1865)

Many great women saints lived out their call to evangelize by instructing children in the faith. Such is the case with St. Madeleine Sophie Barat. Born in Burgundy, France, Madeleine Sophie was raised in a Catholic home. When she was ten years old, her brother Louis, a seminarian, discerned that she was destined to do great things for the kingdom of God. He took it upon himself to educate her in the academic disciplines as well as sacred matters, and to spiritually form her according to the virtues. Madeleine Sophie's education came to a temporary halt when Louis, then ordained, was arrested and imprisoned for two years during the French Revolution. Upon his release, he called Madeleine Sophie to Paris, where he resumed her education.

When the Revolution ended in 1799, the Church in France greatly needed reconstruction, especially its schools. Though Madeleine Sophie wanted to become a Carmelite, under the guidance and direction of her brother Louis and a Father Varin she founded what became the Society of the Sacred Heart, a religious order dedicated to prayer, sacrifice, and the education of girls. With three other companions, Madeleine Sophie made her first consecration in 1800, and professed her vows on June 7, 1802.

As superior of the congregation, Mother Barat quickly established schools throughout Europe and England, and initiated plans to start schools in North America. She journeyed from one convent to another, wrote thousands of letters, counseled cardinals and bishops, and even began retreat work for laywomen.

By the end of her life, Mother Barat had founded 105 schools in all. She was progressive in her educational ideals, and arranged for a general council meeting of her sisters every six years to stay updated on curricula and methods. A champion of women, Mother Barat worked to provide a course of studies that helped her pupils attain the fullness of the feminine ideal. Reflecting on Proverbs 31:10-31, she wrote:

> *How rare it is to find a valiant woman! It is perhaps necessarily so, since Scripture says that they are more precious than pearls and diamonds. Let us however work to train a few. For in this century we must no longer count on men to preserve the faith. The grain of faith that will be saved will hide itself among women. A woman cannot remain neutral in the world. She too is set for the fall and resurrection of many. How different are God's thoughts from ours!*
>
> *Between women and God is often arranged the eternal salvation of husbands and sons. But for this she must be valiant. Strong to uphold purity of life. Strong to keep inviolate the treasure of faith. Strong in every battle of life. Great-souled in the face of calamity, persecution and death. And remember, sorrow is the training ground of strong souls.*

ST. MADELINE SOPHIE BARAT

FAITH IN ACTION

In what ways does St. Madeleine Sophie Barat's quote apply to women in our day and time? Ask yourself: In what specific way(s) can I seek to become more like the "valiant" woman she describes?

Lesson One

Called by God

Prayer to the Holy Spirit

O Holy Spirit, Soul of my soul I adore Thee.
Enlighten, guide, strengthen and console me.
Tell me what I ought to do, then command me to do it.
I promise to be submissive in all that Thou asks of me,
and to accept all that Thou permittest to happen to me,
only show me what is Thy will. Amen.

WEEKLY THEME:
God has created me for a special and unique purpose according to my feminine vocation.

WEEKLY GRACE:
I pray for the grace to recognize my call and mission and its relationship to my femininity.

Full of Grace: Read pages 9 –12 in the text, then answer the following questions.

1. In the Jewish culture, a person's name tells us something important about the essence and character of that person. When the angel Gabriel appears to Mary, he calls her "full of grace." What does this tell us about the state of her soul?

2. If I were to respond to God's invitation to carry Christ "in the womb of my heart," to whom might I be called to bear Him and how, given my state in life?

3. At this point in my life, what obstacles or fears keep me from saying, "yes" to God?

KNOW THE FAITH

God Selects Mary

The Catholic Church teaches that from all eternity God selected Mary to be the mother of the Savior, and enriched Mary with all of the gifts necessary for such a call and mission. One of these gifts was her Immaculate Conception, which means she was preserved from the stain of original sin. This is explained more fully in the *Catechism of the Catholic Church*, paragraphs 490 to 493. Read this passage, then answer the following questions.

1. What is Mary's "Immaculate Conception"? Why was it an important gift for the one called by God to be the mother of the Savior?

___

___

___

___

2. How and when was Mary redeemed?

___

___

___

___

WORD TO KNOW

Dogma: a binding teaching of the Church, which the faithful are compelled to believe. A dogma is revealed by divine revelation either explicitly or implicitly. Explicit revelation is found in the Scriptures; implicit revelation refers to the ongoing Tradition of the Church, starting from the earliest times and continuing in the teaching office of the Magisterium to the present day.

FOR PONDERING...

Mary, My Mother

I came from Judaism into the fullness of the Catholic faith, by way of Evangelical Protestantism. Though I had studied the Scriptures for eighteen years as a Protestant, I had little knowledge of the Woman whom God gave to the world, the Woman first spoken of in Genesis 3:15, through whom our Savior came to crush the seed of the serpent and purchase our salvation on Calvary's Cross.

It was difficult for me to understand the Catholic Church's emphasis and teachings on Mary. How could she have been "conceived without sin" when the Bible says that *all* have sinned and come short of the glory of God?" Why do

Catholics hold her in such high esteem? Why do they consider her their mother, too, and the model for our life in Christ?

Then one day I came across the passage in the first chapter of Luke where the angel Gabriel came to the young Jewish virgin whose name was Mary. The angel delivered to her the most awesome, fearful message ever given a human being: She would bear the very Son of God!

"How could this be?" Mary asked the angel.

Gabriel answered, "*The Holy Spirit will come upon you, and the power of the Most High will overshadow you; therefore the child to be born will be called holy, the Son of God.*"

As a Jew, Mary understood the meaning of Gabriel's words. And because of my Jewish roots, I did, too. My thoughts turned immediately to the Holy of Holies within the Temple. It contained the Ark of the Covenant, which housed the two tablets of stone that Moses had brought down to the Israelites from Mount Sinai. Two cherubim of gold sat on top of the Ark and, when God came to dwell among men through His presence, His Shekinah, His glory, descended upon that Ark. No one — not Moses, not even the High Priest of Israel — could enter that holy place or he would be struck dead (see Exodus 40, especially verses 34-35).

In the first chapter of Luke, the angelic messenger uses the same word for God's indwelling presence to describe what was going to happen to Mary: "*The Holy Spirit will come upon you and the power of the Most High will overshadow you.*" That glorious cloud of God's presence that hovered over the Ark of the Covenant would hover over Mary when she conceived the Son of God!

Now it was my turn to ask the question, "How can this be?" If Moses and the High Priest of Israel would have been struck dead to be so near the presence of God, why wasn't Mary immediately struck dead when the Holy Spirit caused her to conceive? There is only one possible explanation: She must have been sinless, spotless, *full of grace*, just as the angel called her, and just as the Catholic Church has always taught. God intentionally preserved her—kept her free—from the stain of original sin so that she, Mary, could be the Mother of God.

Mary's overshadowing told me more as well. In the Old Testament, the Ark of the Covenant had been God's dwelling place on earth and the sign of His presence with His people. By conceiving the Son of God, Jesus Christ, Mary became God's dwelling place on earth and the sign of His presence with His people, thus fulfilling the prophesy of Isaiah: "*Therefore the Lord himself will give you a sign: the virgin shall be with child, and bear a son, and shall name him Immanuel*" *(7:14)*.

In other words, Mary is the Ark of the *New* Covenant. As the mother of our Lord and Savior, Mary is also the mother of His Church and of His people. This makes her my mother, and yours as well. How could there be a safer, purer, more blessed path to Christ than to remain near Mary His mother, the Woman Full of Grace, whom God gave us to lead us to her Son?

RM

What truth about the Blessed Mother presented here do I find most inspiring and why?

IN CLOSING...

"Behold, I am the handmaid of the Lord. Be it done to me according to Thy word."

BLESSED VIRGIN MARY, LUKE 1:38

Lord, give me the grace and courage to embrace my call and mission as a daughter of God, just as Mary did. Amen.

Lesson Two

The Time for Woman Is Now

Prayer from the Revelations of Saint Brigid

"Blessed art Thou, my Lord, my God, and most beloved Lover of my soul!"

WEEKLY THEME:
God has created me for a special and unique purpose according to my feminine vocation.

WEEKLY GRACE:
I pray for the grace to recognize my call and mission and its relationship to my femininity.

Full of Grace: Read pages 12 - 14 in the text, then answer the following questions.

1. Put into your own words the closing message of the Second Vatican Council Fathers to women. What do these words tell you about your call and mission as a woman in the 21st century?

2. In what ways does the analogy of seed, water, and soil shed light on the receptivity of a woman to new life?

3. What interior reaction do you have to the idea of being gentle and receptive? Does this dimension of your femininity come naturally to you? Why or why not?

4. What "rough exteriors" and "crusty coats" do you think God might want to penetrate in your own life?

KNOW THE FAITH

Mary: Our Mother in the Order of Grace

An encyclical is a letter written by the pope to the universal Church concerning matters of doctrine, morals or discipline, or about significant commemorations. An encyclical calls Catholics to give interior as well as exterior assent and obedience to the teachings it provides.

Redemptoris Mater ("Mother of the Redeemer") is an encyclical written by Pope John Paul II in 1987. In it, the Holy Father gives us clear teaching about Mary's place in God's plan for salvation. Look for the answers to these questions as you read from Paragraph 39 of the Holy Father's encyclical:

1. What two understandings are expressed in Mary's words, "Behold I am the handmaid of the Lord"?

   a. ___

   b. ___

2. With what did Mary's motherhood become "ever more imbued," and what did this quality seek to achieve?

3. Based on this excerpt, what does the phrase "mother in the order of grace" mean?

4. Develop your own definition for "spiritual mother" based on this excerpt from *Redemptoris Mater.*

The words "Behold, I am the handmaid of the Lord" express the fact that from the outset [Mary] accepted and understood her own motherhood as a total gift of self, *a gift of her person to the service of the saving plans of the Most High. And to the very end she lived her entire maternal sharing in the life of Jesus Christ, her Son, in a way that matched her vocation to virginity. ... This basic fact of being the Mother of the Son of God is from the very beginning a complete openness to the person of Christ, to his whole work, to his whole mission. The words "Behold I am the handmaid of the Lord" testify to Mary's openness of spirit: she perfectly unites in herself the love proper to virginity and the love characteristic of motherhood, which are joined and as it were fused together.*

For this reason Mary became not only the "nursing mother" of the Son of Man but also the "associate of unique nobility" of the Messiah and Redeemer. As I have already said, she advanced in her pilgrimage of faith, and in this pilgrimage to the foot of the Cross there was simultaneously accomplished her maternal cooperation with the Savior's whole mission through her actions and sufferings. Along the path of this collaboration with the work of her Son, the Redeemer, Mary's motherhood itself underwent a singular transformation, becoming ever more imbued with "burning charity" towards all those to whom Christ's mission was directed. Through this "burning charity," which sought to achieve, in union with Christ, the restoration of "supernatural life to souls," Mary entered, in a way all her own, into the one mediation "between God and men" which is the mediation of the man Christ Jesus. ...In response to this interior willingness of his Mother, Jesus Christ prepared her *ever more completely to become for all people their "mother in the order of grace"* (MR 39).

WORD TO KNOW

Original Sin: the hereditary stain with which we are born on account of our origin or descent from Adam. The consequences of this stain, even when we are washed clean in baptism, include a disordered will, darkened intellect, and concupiscence of the flesh.

FOR PONDERING...

Midwives

God wants all women to respond with an unqualified "Yes!" to His call. Some of us may feel frightened by the idea that God expects us to change the world—even that little part of the world around us. We look at our own resources and ask, "How can God expect me to solve other people's problems when I can't solve my own?"

If we think that we can rely upon our own limited resources to solve serious problems, we are in real trouble. God is the one who solves the problem — He alone has the answers. Even so, He wants our help. He calls us to be midwives, to assist in the birth of faith in other souls.

Think about the vocation of midwife. A midwife has nothing to do with the conception of the child. She may notice the growth of the child in the womb and encourage the mother, but her real work involves helping the mother through the birth process.

Gail was the midwife of my faith, while I was seeking out the fullness of the faith before joining the Church. The seed had been planted years before, but when I talked to Gail she explained her faith in such a simple way. Her words helped me through the birth process.

As midwives of faith, we are called to help our friends through the process of conversion. As God's grace settles deep in another person's heart, a desire to know God begins to grow. If a soul isn't open to faith, as midwives we can pray that God will work in that person's life until she has a change of heart toward Him. Until that time, there is little we can do.

Once God has planted the seed of faith in the open soul, however, slowly the desire grows and we, the midwives, may notice that our friend or coworker is pregnant with faith. She starts asking questions. She responds more positively when you talk about your faith. And then the day will come — in God's good time — for the faith that was growing in her to manifest itself.

This conversion process is different for everyone. Some struggle, some fight, and some have easy deliveries. We, the midwives, merely guide the natural process. We give encouragement to the soul in labor, soothing, comforting, guiding the process. And when faith bursts forth, we provide care during the first moments. The child is not ours but God's. He is ultimately responsible for the soul's continued growth, just as He was for its conception.

DO'L

Who are three "midwives" in my life and what have they "brought to birth" in me? Have I been a "midwife" for someone in his/her faith? Who and how?

IN CLOSING...

"O Jesus, I promise to submit myself to all that You permit to befall me, make me only know Your Will. My most sweet Jesus, infinitely merciful God, most tender Father of souls, and in a particular way of the most weak, most miserable, most infirm which You carry with special tenderness between Your divine arms, I come to You to ask You, through the love and merits of Your Sacred Heart, the grace to comprehend and to do always Your holy Will, the grace to confide in You, the grace to rest securely through time and eternity in Your loving divine arms."

ST. GIANNA BERETTA MOLLA

Lord, help me with feminine intuition to recognize when I am being called to assist in the birth of new life, especially spiritual life. Amen.

Lesson Three

The Influence of Woman's Vocation

WEEKLY THEME:
God has created me for a special and unique purpose according to my feminine vocation.

WEEKLY GRACE:
I pray for the grace to recognize my call and mission and its relationship to my femininity.

Prayer: Hail Holy Queen

Hail Holy Queen, Mother of Mercy, our life, our sweetness, and our hope.
To you do we cry, poor banished children of Eve.
To you do we send up our sighs, mourning and weeping in this valley of tears.
Turn then, O most gracious advocate, your eyes of mercy toward us;
and after this, our exile, show unto us the blessed fruit of your womb, Jesus!
O clement, O loving, O sweet Virgin Mary!
Pray for us O holy Mother of God,
that we may be made worthy of the promises of Christ.
Amen

Full of Grace: Read pages 14 –19 in the text, then answer the following questions.

1. What spiritual reality is mirrored in a woman's physical potentiality to bring forth new life?

2. Why and how are consecrated religious women and celibate single women still called to motherhood?

3. What does the Greek word *munus* mean? What is woman's *munus* and what about her helps her to carry it out?

4. In what specific ways am I living out this *munus*? How can I grow in this call?

KNOW THE FAITH

The Hour Is Now

The last general meeting of the Second Vatican Council was held on December 7, 1965. On December 8, 1965, Pope Paul VI and various cardinals addressed different groups of people. The closing message, *To Women,* was read by Leon Cardinal Duval of Algiers, Algeria, assisted by Julius Cardinal Doepfner of Munich, Germany, and Raul Cardinal Silva of Santiago, Chile. This letter is prescient in its content and as timely now as when it was first delivered. Once you have read the excerpt below, answer the questions that follow.

1. What characteristic will help woman aid humanity in not falling?

2. According to the letter, what are some of the ways women influence the world in a way unique from men?

3. Which of the "womanly virtues" mentioned in this letter do I most need to acquire?

And now it is to you that we address ourselves, women of all states — girls, wives, mothers and widows, to you also, consecrated virgins and women living alone — you constitute half of the immense human family. As you know, the Church is proud to have glorified and liberated woman, and in the course of the centuries, in diversity of characters, to have brought into relief her basic equality with man. But the hour is coming, in fact has come, when the vocation of woman is being achieved in its fullness, the hour in which woman acquires in the world an influence, an effect and a power never hitherto achieved. That is why, at this moment when the human race is under-going so deep a transformation, women impregnated with the spirit of the Gospel can do so much to aid humanity in not falling.

You women have always had as your lot the protection of the home, the love of beginnings and an understanding of cradles. You are present in the mystery of a life beginning. You offer consolation in the departure of death. Our technology runs the risk of becoming inhuman. Reconcile men with life and above all, we beseech you, watch carefully over the future of our race. Hold back the hand of man who, in a moment of folly, might attempt to destroy human civilization.

Wives, mothers of families, the first educators of the human race in the intimacy of the family circle, pass on to your sons and your daughters the traditions of your fathers at the same time that you prepare them for an unsearchable future. Always remember that by her children a mother belongs to that future which perhaps she will not see.

And you, women living alone, realize what you can accomplish through your dedicated vocation. Society is appealing to you on all sides. Not even families can live without the help of those who have no families. Especially you, consecrated virgins, in a world where egoism and the search for pleasure would become law, be the guardians of purity, unselfishness and piety. Jesus who has given to conjugal love all its plenitudes, has also exalted the renouncement of human love when this is for the sake of divine love and for the service of all.

Lastly, women in trial, who stand upright at the foot of the cross like Mary, you who so often in history have given to men the strength to battle unto the very end and to give witness to the point of martyrdom, aid them now still once more to retain courage in their great undertakings, while at the same time maintaining patience and an esteem for humble beginnings.

Women, you do know how to make truth sweet, tender and accessible, make it your task to bring the spirit of this council into institutions, schools, homes and daily life. Women of the entire universe, whether Christian or non-believing, you to whom life is entrusted at this grave moment in history, it is for you to save the peace of the world.

WORD TO KNOW

Vocation: From the Latin verb "vocare," meaning "to call." A call by God to an individual in which a path or state of life is revealed which will bring that soul to God in the most efficacious way.

FOR PONDERING...
The Influence of Mothers

Developmental psychologists who study little babies have come to some remarkable conclusions. At one time people believed that babies' minds were blank slates. Now there is evidence that from the moment the baby is born, she is pre-programmed to attach to her mother. The baby has heard Mama's voice in the womb, and is born to look for her mother's smiling face and the spark of light in her eyes. And mothers have a natural instinct to lean close to their baby and smile. This bonding between mother and child—whether or not they are biologically related—is absolutely crucial to the development of that infant.

Through this interaction between mother and child, connections are built in the baby's brain, connections that form the foundation for the child's emotional development. A baby who is securely attached, whose mother has smiled an cooed during the first months will — for the rest of her life — have an image of love imprinted on her brain and thus go through life feeling secure.

Unfortunately, sometimes it happens that a baby doesn't securely attach. The mother may sincerely love her baby, but just not be able to give that baby what she needs in the critical firsts. Perhaps the mother is ill or unavoidably absent, depressed or angry. Or maybe she was so little nurtured herself that her "mothering" instincts are not what they should be. When this happens, the child grows up with an empty place inside where the picture of her mother's loving smile is supposed to be.

That's why God needs spiritual mothers—women who can "mother" unmothered children. Our positive influence on others begins when we have a heart for their well-being. Whenever possible, we must try to reconcile these unmothered souls with their natural mothers; when that is impossible, we must bring them to Mary, who is the perfect mother of us all.

Do you have a friend who has revealed to you an empty place in her heart? Remind yourself that she probably doesn't need more "good advice." She knows that her life is in disorder. What she needs is someone who will look in her eyes and say with tenderness, "God really loves you and so do I."

DO'L

What women has God placed in my path to mother me besides my own mother? Is the Blessed Mother an active "mother" in my life? Who might God be asking me to "mother" besides my own children?

____

____

____

IN CLOSING...

"By union with God we shall gain hearts. . . . Without this union we will but make a little noise."

ST. JULIE BILLIART

Lord Jesus, show me your heart for the people you put in my life as spiritual sons and daughters. Mary, pray for me, that I might radiate your motherly love. Amen.

Lesson Four

Impregnated with the Spirit of the Gospel

Prayer

Saint Michael the Archangel, defend us in battle;
be our protection against the wickedness and the
snares of the devil.
May God rebuke him, we humbly pray,
and do thou, O Prince of the Heavenly Host,
by the power of God, thrust into hell Satan
and all the evil spirits
who prowl about the world seeking the ruin of souls. Amen.

WEEKLY THEME:
God has created me for a special and unique purpose according to my feminine vocation.

WEEKLY GRACE:
I pray for the grace to recognize my call and mission and its relationship to my femininity.

Full of Grace: Read pages 19 –21 in the text, then answer the following questions.

1. What does it mean to become "impregnated" with the Gospel?

2. Using Cardinal Ratzinger's comparison of Mary's motherhood to a field, describe how we can become impregnated with a spirit of the gospel.

3. What is Mary's *munus* and how does she carry it out?

4. Have I surrendered myself completely to God so that I might radiate "that divine energy that initiates others into God's own life?" If not, what prevents me from doing so (consider fears, concerns, misconceptions, attachments, sins, etc.)?

KNOW THE FAITH

Carrying The Word of God to the World

The Church exists to evangelize. It is her primary call and mission. As members of the Body of Christ, we, too, are called to evangelize. Like Mary, we are called to carry the Word of God to the world. The Second Vatican Council's "Decree on the Apostolate of the Laity" (*Apostolicam Actuositatem*) gives us good guidance and instruction on "restoring the temporal order." Read the paragraphs from this document that are printed below, then answer the following questions.

1. Paragraph six says that one of the ways we evangelize is with the witness of our lives. What are the two opportunities we have to announce Christ by our words?

   a. ______

   b. ______

2. What "new problems" in our own time call for increased efforts in evangelization?

3. On what does the success of the lay apostolate depend?

4. Why is the Blessed Virgin Mary the perfect example of evangelization?

(AA 6) The mission of the Church looks to the salvation of men, which is to be achieved by belief in Christ and by His grace. The apostolate therefore of the Church and of all its members is primarily directed to manifest Christ's message by words and deeds and to communicate His grace to the world...

There are innumerable opportunities open to the laity for the exercise of the apostolate of evangelization and sanctification. The very testimony of their Christian life and good works done in a supernatural spirit have the power to draw men to the faith and to God...

However, an apostolate of this kind consists not only in the witness of one's life; a true apostle looks for opportunities to announce Christ by words addressed either to non-believers with a view to leading them to faith, or to the faithful with a view to instructing, strengthening, and encouraging them to a more fervent life...

Since, in our own times, new problems are arising and very serious errors are circulating which tend to undermine completely religion, the moral order, and human society itself, this holy Council earnestly exhorts laymen — each according to his natural endowments and training — to be more diligent in doing their part to explain, defend, and properly apply Christian principles to the problems of our era in accordance with the mind of the Church.

(AA 4) ...it is evident that the success of the lay apostolate depends upon the laity's living union with Christ, according to the Lord's words,"He who abides in me, and I in him, bears much fruit, for without me you can do nothing: (John 15:5) ... In this way the laity must make progress in holiness in a happy and ready spirit, trying prudently and patiently to overcome difficulties... Such a life requires a continual exercise of faith, hope, and charity.

The perfect example of this type of spiritual and apostolic life is the most Blessed Virgin Mary, Queen of Apostles, who while leading a life common to all here on earth, one filled with family concerns and labors, was always intimately united with her Son and in an entirely unique way cooperated in the work of the Savior. Having now been assumed into heaven, with her maternal love she cares for the brothers of her Son who are still on their earthly pilgrimage and remain involved in dangers and difficulties until they are led into the happy fatherland. All should most devoutly venerate her and commend their life and apostolate to her maternal care.

WORD TO KNOW

Apostolate: Refers to the mission of the Church to carry on the redemptive work of Jesus Christ, to be expressed in ways appropriate to each vocation. There is the Apostolate of the Hierarchy, the Apostolate of Priests, the Apostolate of Religious, and the Apostolate of the Lay Faithful.

The Apostolate of the Lay Faithful is exercised by the laity in the ordinary duties of daily life — within the family, the workforce, the social and political spheres, and the professions. By virtue of our baptism, each of us has been called to contribute to the sanctification of the world.

FOR PONDERING...

Women Who Changed History

In the Old Testament, women such as Miriam, Deborah, and Judith were leaders among their people, and changed the course of history by their actions. In the New Testament, Our Lady's "Yes" to the angel Gabriel ushered in the New Covenant. Through her apparitions at Guadalupe, Mary has evangelized millions of people in Mexico and Central and South America.

A great many other holy women have influenced the course of Church history as well. Saints Catherine of Siena, Joan of Arc, Brigid of Sweden, Teresa of Avila, Katharine Drexel, and Venerable Conchita are just a few outstanding examples of women who were active forces of change in the world. However, those hidden in cloisters or devoted primarily to their own families have through their prayerful witness had untold influence as well. Saints Therese of Lisieux and Gianna Beretta Molla are just two such examples.

God has filled women from every walk of life with graces for transforming the world. Whether consecrated religious, single women, or wives and mothers, each of these women understood the importance of their gifts for the time and age into which they were born. Woman is a transmitter of life not only through the babies she carries in her womb, but also in her spiritual motherhood.

Because of the "reach" of media today, the influence of women may be read, heard, or seen even more clearly. Women transmit Christian life whenever they influence culture and society. Two of the greatest "mothers" of the 20th century—Blessed Mother Teresa of Calcutta, and Mother Angelica, foundress of EWTN—have no biological children. And yet, their ministries reach millions of people; they are "Mother" not only because of their affiliation within a religious community, but out of the gratitude of their spiritual children, the beneficiaries of their motherly love.

As Saint Edith Stein understood it, precisely because a woman's body is able to house another human being, women are created body and soul for person-to-person intimacy. Our motherly hearts have empathy for those who suffer, making us eager to find ways to help those in need whether by picking up the destitute and dying off the street, bringing the truth through television and radio to those in doubt, or soothing a child in pain.

Ask God to show you how He wants you to answer the call to motherhood today.

RC

What unique circumstances in my life set me apart and provide me with a path of holiness that only I can pursue?

IN CLOSING...

"I love you and pray for all of you as if you were my own, and you are. To young kids, I'm a grandmother, to others a mother, to most of you a nun, and to all of you a friend. God loves you."

MOTHER ANGELICA

Lord Jesus, from the cross you gave your Mother to every soul you died to save.
Help me to see in every soul Your Mother's beloved child. Amen.

Lesson Five

Called to Radiate the Love of Christ

Prayer: The Memorare

Remember, O most gracious Virgin Mary, that never was it known
that anyone who fled to your protection,
implored your help, or sought your intercession, was left unaided.
Inspired with this confidence, I fly to you,
O Virgin of virgins, my Mother!
To you I come; before you I stand, sinful and sorrowful.
O Mother of the Word Incarnate, despise not my petitions,
But, in your mercy, hear and answer me. Amen

WEEKLY THEME:
God has created me for a special and unique purpose according to my feminine vocation.

WEEKLY GRACE:
I pray for the grace to recognize my call and mission and its relationship to my femininity.

Full of Grace: Read pages 21 –25 in the text, and then answer the following questions.

1. Truly happy women have an inner glow that transcends daily anxieties. They shine from within, reflecting the light of their heavenly Father. Who are some women I know who radiate these virtues of the Blessed Virgin: self-offering love, strength in sorrow, fidelity and devotion in work, intuition, support, and encouragement?

2. Which of these "radiant" qualities describe me? (Hint: Which of these qualities have others noticed in you? Which do you tend to notice most quickly in others?)

3. St. Teresa Benedicta of the Cross (Edith Stein) said that Jesus stands in the center of Mary's life. To what extent would she say that about me? Upon what would she base her answer?

4. What are the three dispositions of heart that mark a handmaid of the Lord?

KNOW THE FAITH

Mary Shows Us Who We Are To Be

Lumen Gentium is the document from the Second Vatican Council that concerns the Church. In it we find the Council's teaching about the Blessed Virgin Mary. In Paragraphs 63 to 65, Mary is called a "type" of the Church. In its biblical sense, a "type" is a person, thing, action or event that foreshadows the future. A "type" also means the individual who realizes the ideal. Mary fulfills both of these definitions as a type of the Church. Read for yourself this section of the Council document, then answer the following questions.

1. In what three ways does the Church reflect Mary?

   a. ______

   b. ______

   c. ______

2. How is Mary the "pattern of virtue" of the faithful?

In the mystery of the Church, which is itself rightly called mother and virgin, the Blessed Virgin Mary played a leading role, providing an example as virgin and mother in an eminent and unique way. In faith and obedience she brought forth on earth the very Son of the Father: She who knew not man was overshadowed by the Holy Spirit. As a new Eve she believed, not the serpent of old but the messenger of God, with a faith wholly free from doubt. She gave birth to the Son, appointed by God to be the firstborn among many brothers, *that is, among those who believe; with a mother's love she cooperates in their birth and development.*

The Church contemplates the depth of her holiness, imitates her charity and in fidelity brings to completion the Father's will; she herself becomes a mother through the word of God received in faith. Through preaching and by baptism she brings forth to new and everlasting life children conceived by the Holy Spirit and born of God. She is herself a virgin, preserving with integrity and purity the faith she has reposed in her Spouse. She imitates the mother of her Lord, and by the power of the Holy Spirit treasures with virginal purity faith in all its fullness, hope in all its certainty, love in all its sincerity.

In the person of the Blessed Virgin the Church already possesses the perfection by which it stands without spot or wrinkle; but the faithful still strive to grow in holiness as they conquer sin. So they lift their eyes to Mary, shining above the whole community of God's elect as the pattern of virtue. As the Church lovingly reflects on her and contemplates her in the light of the Word made man, it reverently enters more deeply into the surpassing mystery of the incarnation and takes on more and more the likeness of its Spouse.

Mary, because she has entered intimately into the history of salvation, in a certain sense gathers up in her own person the great truths of the faith and awakens their resonance when she is the object of preaching and veneration; she summons the faithful to her Son, to his sacrifice and to the Father's love. In seeking to further the glory of Christ, the Church becomes more and more like Mary, its exalted type, as it continues its progress in faith, hope, and charity, seeking and fulfilling the divine will in all things.

So also in its apostolic task the Church rightly looks to the one who bore Christ, Christ who was conceived by the Holy Spirit and born of the Virgin in order that he might also be born and grow in the hearts of the faithful. In her whole life this virgin mother showed herself as an example of that motherly love that must animate all who share in the apostolic mission of the Church for the regeneration of mankind.

WORD TO KNOW

Shine: A number of Greek words are translated "shine." Three of these are *phaino* ("The light *shines* in the darkness and the darkness comprehended it not," John 1:5), *lampo* ("Let your light *shine* [like a torch] among men," Matthew 5:16), and *eklampo* ("Then the righteous shall *shine forth* as the sun in the kingdom of the father," Matthew 13:43).

FOR PONDERING...

Radiant From Within

Quite a number of Catholic women have difficulty identifying with the mother of Jesus. The statues in our churches depict Mary perfectly still and quiet, leading us to imagine her as an apparition rather than a flesh-and-blood woman in Nazareth. Surely in her motherly warmth, Mary our mother felt tender concern for all in need in her town as well as for the disciples of her Son. Surely those people were recipients of Our Lady's intuition, comfort, helpful advice, and deeds.

Many of us have some of the womanly gifts described in this lesson (for example fidelity, encouragement, and intuition). Often, though, we are so focused on our shortcomings that we don't thank God for the good we do by radiating authentic love for others. When others praise our virtues, we think, "That was nothing; it was easy for me." And yet, it is easy precisely *because* it is a gift from God.

St. Teresa Benedicta of the Cross is quoted in *Full of Grace* (page 24), saying that our deepest longing is to surrender ourselves totally to God. In moments of grace, we do give ourselves to Him in this way. But then, later on, we forget and surrender to our idols instead: We try to please others at the expense of God's will; allow our desire for earthly treasure to keep us from being generous to the poor; desperately cling to disordered relationships.

However, if we allow it, God can heal us of the insecurities that lead to attachments to lesser goods. Through a deeper and more honest prayer life, however, we may begin to draw closer to God Himself, the greatest good of all.

Begin by setting aside a designated time of prayer each day. Some spiritual advisors recommend making your personal prayer time a daily appointment with God. It is good to use the beautiful words of traditional prayers, but it is also necessary to pray from our negative feelings. An example might be, "Dear loving God, I am bedeviled with anxieties about losing worldly things or relationships. Help me to fall in love with *You* so that I can seek your gifts with less desperation."

RC

Is there anything in my life that might be considered an "idol"? What strategy or strategies can I employ to put it in its proper place?

____

____

____

____

IN CLOSING...

"We should not wish for anything but what comes to us from moment to moment, exercising ourselves nonetheless for good."

ST. CATHERINE OF GENOA

Father God, You knit me together in my mother's womb, and knew me long before my eyes opened on this world. Help me to trust Your benevolent goodness. Amen.

Chapter Two

Prayer: Strength of the Abundant Life

Full of Grace: This week covers pages 27-44 of the text.

There are as many definitions of prayer as there are persons who pray. Essentially, prayer is how we approach God, and how we cultivate a strong personal relationship with Him. As with all relationships, there are some general principles we must follow to protect our spiritual health and to avoid confusion. And yet, within those boundaries we can anticipate a uniquely intimate exchange with the Divine.

Prayer is the key to strong spiritual health. Many women saints left us prayers that leap off the page for joy, expressing sheer delight in the company of their Lord. Other saints recorded their struggles, and how they persevered when their souls felt "dry" and far from God. Some pour out their anguish in times of trial. Here, too, are the ordinary daily expressions of ordinary women—like ourselves! In these pages we pray that you'll find inspiration for your own prayer life.

In this chapter we will learn different methods for prayer. Some of these methods or modes of prayer may be familiar, but untried; others will be altogether new to you, a revelation about how to pray. As you work through these pages, be generous with your time. Women who have learned to pray deeply often discover that time seems to "stretch" in other areas of life. No time spent in prayer is ever wasted. Our prayers invite Jesus to continue His work in us, to bring to completion the purpose for which He created us. As you turn your thoughts again and again toward God, *you* will experience true transformation and renewal. When this happens, you will find yourself able to serve God in ways you never thought possible, and to do wonders in the world around you.

This week we will look at what the Church teaches about five aspects of prayer, and how you can begin to put these prayer forms into practice in your own life.

LESSON ONE — Prayer Power
LESSON TWO — Vocal Prayer
LESSON THREE — Meditation
LESSON FOUR — Contemplation: The Divine Life Within
LESSON FIVE — The Effects of Prayer

Questions to Ponder This Week

- In what areas of my life would I most like God to transform me?
- How does prayer initiate that process of transformation?
- How does each mode of prayer fulfill a distinct purpose in God's plan for my life?
- How does Christian prayer unify the Body of Christ?

Media Response Sheet

Prayer, Strength of the Abundant Life

Answer the following questions as you watch the pre-recorded lesson given by Johnnette S. Benkovic, founder of Women of Grace®.

WEEKLY THEME
Supported by consistent prayer, my daily life will be transformed.

WEEKLY GRACE
I pray for the grace to have a regular, established time of prayer each day.

1. ____________________ and ____________________ seem to go hand in hand. And, when we make a decision for the Lord, ____________________ seem to increase. Why is this so?

____

____

2. Our call is always to be ____________________ to those around us, and to awaken the ____________________ in them. Who is our exemplar? ____________________

____

____

3. What are three ways we can cooperate with the will of the Father?

____

____

What is the first step to growing in these three ways, and why?

____

____

4. What is prayer? What definition do you find in the *Catechism of the Catholic Church*? How does St. Teresa of Avila define prayer? ____________________

____

____

5. What are the two kinds of vocal prayer?

a. ______

b. ______

6. What is the key to praying formulated prayers?

______

______

7. Spontaneous vocal prayer yields to...

______

______

______

8. Mental prayer is essentially ______ speaking to ______.

9. What are the four faculties of Christian meditation, according to the *Catechism of the Catholic Church*?

a. ______

b. ______

c. ______

d. ______

10. Fill in the acronym to see how we enter into Sacred Scripture:

P: ______

R: ______

A: ______

Y: ______

11. How do we know when our prayer is becoming contemplation?

______

______

______

12. Encounters with God are______.

Woman of Grace

St. Teresa of Avila (1515-1582)

St. Teresa of Avila shows us it is never too late to get serious about our prayer life. Born Dona Teresa Sanchez Cepeda Davila y Ahumada, Teresa was an active child with a big imagination and great sensitivity of heart. Little Teresa and her brother Roderigo were intrigued by the lives of the saints and the martyrs, and often sought to imitate their holy example.

When Teresa was fourteen, her mother died. This was a turning point in the young woman's life. The young cousin who came to keep Teresa company had worldly ways that greatly influenced the young saint. One of their pastimes was reading tales of chivalry and romance, of which Teresa later wrote, "*These tales did not fail to cool my good desires, and were the cause of my falling insensibly into other defects.*"

Teresa's father, Don Alonzo, was not blind to the change in his daughter; he decided to send her to an Augustinian convent, to be educated among other girls of her social class. A serious illness interrupted Teresa's education, however, and she was brought home to recuperate.

After her recovery she spent time at the home of a pious uncle, who gave her the *Letters of St. Jerome* to read. These letters sparked a desire in her heart for religious life but her father withheld his consent. Fearing that if she waited she would lose her resolve, Teresa sneaked away and secretly entered the Carmelite Convent of the Incarnation outside the city of Avila. One year later, after making her profession, she was once again struck by a serious sickness. Don Alonzo removed her from the convent and, after a period of intense illness, she began to regain her health.

This time, her devout uncle gave Teresa a book by Father Francis de Osuna, which introduced Teresa to the prayer of recollection and the prayer of quiet. This book led her in the practice of mental prayer, from which she soon progressed to more advanced stages of contemplation. After three years, Teresa went back to the convent. Sixteenth-century convent life was not conducive to prayer. Young nuns were permitted to receive guests in the convent parlor, and Teresa soon found her time filled with visitors and idle conversation. She soon gave up the practice of mental prayer altogether, a decision she later regretted.

By the time Teresa finally returned to the practice of mental prayer she was thirty-nine years old and had been a nun for twenty years. She was never to abandon her life of prayer again. As her interior life progressed, Teresa was given extraordinary visions and locutions; these brought her closer to God and yet convicted her of her shortcomings. In time, she translated her insights into a classic spiritual work called *The Interior Castle*, a book comparable in its theological weight and significance to St. Augustine's *Confessions*.

Eventually, Teresa moved out of the Carmel of the Incarnation, and established the Discalced (shoeless) Carmelite order, which kept a more primitive (ascetic) rule of life. Despite great difficulties and persecution, she founded sixteen other houses throughout Spain, and died at one of these houses at the age of 67. Because of her enormous theological contribution to the Church especially in the realm of prayer, she was declared a Doctor of the Church.

> *"An intelligent mind is simple and teachable; it sees its faults and allows itself to be guided. A mind that is dull and narrow never sees its faults even when shown to them. It is always pleased with itself and never learns to do right."*
>
> ST. TERESA OF AVILA

FAITH IN ACTION

Like St. Teresa, we often become ensnared by distractions and circumstances that tempt us to forsake our commitment to pray. What excuses do you most commonly use? Ask yourself, "How can I increase my resolve?"

Woman of Grace

St. Gertrude the Great (1256 – 1301?)

The nuns of the Benedictine Abbey at Helfta in Saxony would have been surprised to hear that Gertrude, their bright and engaging pupil, would one day be called "the great" because of the depth of her prayer life rather than for her academic achievements. The community did not consider Gertrude to be particularly zealous or pious. And, indeed, for her first twenty-five years she was not.

Shortly after her twenty-fifth birthday, Gertrude had an encounter with the risen Lord, who promised to free her from the emotional depression and spiritual distress she had been battling. "Do not fear," He told her. "I will save you and set you free." From that moment on, Gertrude was favored with visions and a level of mystical prayer that transformed her life. She gave up her academic studies and began to pursue the interior life and the study of Sacred Scripture. At the request of Our Lord, she began to record the insights and spiritual understandings she received. Many of these writings have been lost; however, some of them, such as *The Herald of Divine Love*, have been preserved.

The foundation of Gertrude's spiritual life was the Sacred Heart of Jesus. In the Sacred Heart she experienced the humanity of Jesus and the infinite depth of His love for us. She saw His most Sacred Heart as a treasury of graces ready to be dispensed upon the sinner at the least movement of repentance. Jesus gave St. Gertrude visions of His Sacred Heart. In these visions, St. John the Beloved Disciple was often present. During one of these visions, St. Gertrude asked St. John, "Why is it, O beloved of God, that you who rested on His bosom at the Last Supper have said nothing of what you experienced then?"

St. John answered her, "It was my task to present to the first age of the Church the doctrine of the Word made flesh, which no human intellect can ever fully comprehend. The eloquence of that sweet beating of His Heart is reserved for the last age in order that the world grown cold and torpid may be set on fire with the love of God."

St. Gertrude had a particular burden for the souls in purgatory. This burden was placed upon her heart by other visions the Lord gave her. In one such vision, Gertrude saw a table upon which were placed many expensive pearls. She was given to understand that the pearls represented the prayers for the holy souls. All at the same time, St. Gertrude saw souls being freed from suffering and ascending like bright sparks to heaven.

In another vision, Our Lord told Gertrude that He longed for someone to ask Him to release souls from purgatory to heaven. And in still another vision, the Lord told the saint that He would release a thousand souls from purgatory every time the following prayer was prayed:

> *Eternal Father, I offer Thee the Most Precious Blood of Thy Divine Son, Jesus, in union with the Masses said throughout the world today, for all the Holy Souls in purgatory, for sinners everywhere, for sinners in the universal church, those in my own home and within my family. Amen.*

These visions of Jesus continued until the end of Gertrude's life. In her last moments, Jesus said to her, "Come, my chosen one, and I will place you on My throne." In 1677 Pope Clement XII proclaimed that St. Gertrude's feast be observed throughout the Church. One biography of the saint says that she may well be the leading woman writer and visionary of thirteenth century monastic culture. Clearly, though she lived more than six hundred years ago, St. Gertrude gives example and insight for all women of the third millennium.

FAITH IN ACTION

Consider St. John's statement to Gertrude about the Sacred Heart. What about our day and time might indicate that this may well be the time to "hear" the "eloquence of the sweet beating" of the Sacred Heart of Jesus? What about this time in my own life?

Lesson One

Prayer Power

Prayer: The Magnificat (Luke 1:49-50)
"The mighty God has done great things for me, and
Holy is His name.
His mercy reaches from age to age."

WEEKLY THEME
Supported by consistent prayer, my daily life will be transformed.

WEEKLY GRACE
I pray for the grace to have a regular, established time of prayer each day.

Full of Grace: Read pages 27–31 in the text, then answer the following questions.

1. Daughters naturally seek a special relationship with their fathers. As daughters of God, we have a perfect Father, worthy of our trust. Can you think of a time when you were especially aware of God's love and care?

____

____

____

2. God's ____________________ is the means He has provided for us to come to Him. We come to the ____________________ through ____________________.

3. How does the intimacy of a relationship with another human person compare to the kind of intimacy God wants to have with us? In what ways are they similar?

____

____

____

4. What are the three main categories of prayer?

   a. ____

   b. ____

   c. ____

KNOW THE FAITH

The Rosary: A Way to Contemplation

The Rosary is an ancient prayer form that incorporates all three categories of prayer. Its name is derived from the word *rosarius*, meaning a garland or bouquet of roses. This popular devotion has been practiced in the Church for more than a thousand years.

Initially, monks strung pebbles or bone fragments on a rope and used it to count their prayers. By the thirteenth century, these ropes were manufactured by an honored craft guild, and were widely called "Paternosters," the Latin name for the "Our Father," which at the time was the predominant prayer of this devotion. The Hail Mary as we know it was not used until the twelfth century; it was gradually added until the Rosary grew into its present form.

Until recently, fifteen Christian mysteries were associated with the Rosary: five joyful, five sorrowful, and five glorious. Each of these mysteries was reflected upon for the time it took to pray ten Hail Mary's, represented by ten beads (called a "decade"), followed by a single Our Father. The Rosary is "Christocentric," for each mystery is intimately connected to the life and work of Jesus. On October 16, 2002, Pope John Paul II signed an apostolic letter called *Rosarium Virginis Mariae* ("The Rosary of the Virgin Mary"). In it he suggested that the faithful consider adding five additional mysteries to the prayer of the Rosary. These "Luminous Mysteries" or "Mysteries of Light" focused on the public ministry of Jesus.

Implicit in the Holy Father's letter is the fact that the Rosary incorporates all three forms of prayer — vocal prayer, meditation, and contemplation. The "repetition" of the Rosary is designed to help the one who prays to assimilate the mysteries of Christ's life through meditation. Consequently, the prayer of the Rosary "engages the whole person in all his complex psychological, physical, and relational reality, a characteristic common to Christian spirituality" (No. 27).

The Holy Father also suggested that the very design of the Rosary takes on "a symbolism which can give added depth to contemplation" (No. 36). The circular set of beads fashioned around the Crucifix indicates that the life and prayer of the believer is to be centered on Christ: "Everything begins from him, everything leads towards him, everything through him, in the Holy Spirit attains to the Father."

According to the Holy Father, the beads provide a "counting mechanism" that mark the progress of the prayer evoking the "unending path of contemplation and of Christian perfection," while the "sweet chain" that links the beads binds us to God as Father and puts us in tune with Mary and Christ himself. The beads also "remind us of our many relationships, of the bond of communion and fraternity which unites us all in Christ."

The prayers of the Rosary themselves continue to aid our union with God. Although the Hail Mary is "the most substantial element in the Rosary and also the one that makes it a Marian prayer *par excellence*" (No. 33), the Holy Father points out that this prayer is also profoundly Christological, for it gives us a "glimpse of God's own wonderment as he contemplates his 'masterpiece' — the Incarnation of the Son in the womb of the Virgin Mary."

In his letter, the Holy Father draws our attention to the central position of *the name of Jesus* in the prayer, and refers to it as the *hinge* that joins together the two parts of the Hail Mary. It is the prayer's *center of gravity*, establishing the relationship between Mary and Christ, that gives us the confidence to entrust ourselves to her maternal intercession.

Pope John Paul II closes his beautiful letter by exhorting families to once again make the Rosary a part of their family prayer. He encourages all parents to entrust to the Rosary the growth and development of their children. "To pray the Rosary *for children*, and even more, *with children*, training them from their earliest years to experience this daily 'pause for prayer' with the family, is admittedly not the solution to every problem, but it is a spiritual aid which should not be underestimated." Prayed with consistency, faithfulness, and devotion, those who make the Rosary part of their prayer life can expect to learn "the secret of peace and make it his life's project."

1. Briefly explain how the Rosary incorporates all three categories of prayer.

____

____

____

2. Which of the Holy Father's insights about the Rosary will help me pray this prayer with greater devotion? Why?

____

____

____

WORD TO KNOW

Devotion: A prayer or other external practice of piety that reveals a desire to be at the service of God. True devotion may focus directly upon God in worship and adoration, or indirectly through the veneration of the Blessed Mother or the saints, the "first fruits" of God's salvific work. When practiced with sincerity of heart, devotions promote an ardent and active life of faith. Popular devotions include the Rosary, the Stations of the Cross, honoring First Fridays and First Saturdays, enthroning pictures of the Sacred Heart of Jesus and the Immaculate Heart of Mary in the home, and many other acts of piety.

FOR PONDERING…

Praying With Love and Devotion

I'll never forget the Christmas Eve that I visited a Catholic church for the first time. My brother, David, was actually thinking of becoming Catholic — of all things! — and I desperately wanted to stop him. Thanks be to God, I could not stop him. But I'll never forget walking into that little church in upstate New York and sitting through what I would later learn is the greatest prayer of the Church — the Mass.

I was shocked to discover that the prayers sounded much like those I prayed as a child with my family: "Blessed are you, Lord, God of all creation," the priest prayed at the beginning of the liturgy of the Eucharist. "Through your goodness we have this bread to sanctify, which earth has given and human hands have made. It will become for us the bread of life." Every Friday night we used to pray these words in my Jewish home as we gathered around the Sabbath table: "Baruch ata Adonai, Eloheynu, Melech ha Olam hamotzi lechem min ha aretz." ("Blessed art thou O Lord our God, Ruler of the universe, who brings forth bread from the earth.")

Seventeen years passed before I, too, entered the Catholic Church and received from that altar the true Bread of Life, the Jewish Messiah. However, long before this happened I learned that all of our Catholic prayers are rooted in the Old Testament Scriptures. Every prayer of our Blessed Mother, of Simeon, of Zechariah, and of our Lord Himself is rooted in the Old Testament Psalms and Prophets. Our Lady drew her Magnificat -- her hymn of praise and thanksgiving — from the Psalms as well as the prayer of Hannah in the first book of Samuel. Like the souls of the apostles, Mary's soul had been steeped in the Jewish Scriptures; consequently, their knowledge of and love for God was reflected in their prayers.

I knew that our prayers, like those of our faithful ancestors, should also reflect our knowledge and love of God. Our Father in Heaven desires that we know Him. He desires that our hearts become filled with love of Him, He Who is the God of Israel, the God who became Man for us, and who died and rose that we might have life.

How can we enter into that love and knowledge more deeply? Four key actions can help us grow in this way:

First, unite your heart with God and come to Him as a child with a child's heart. Do not fear. He loves you and gave Himself for you.

Second, begin your day with prayer. I awake every morning and thank God that I am Catholic and that He has given me knees to bend. If you haven't begun your day in prayer, start by getting out of bed, come before God on your knees and say, "Good morning, Lord. Thank you for giving me this day. Please help me to love you today in everyone I see — in my husband, my children, my co-workers, that difficult neighbor. Help me to love them as you love me. Amen."

Third, pray as a family. Don't let your children leave the house in the morning without praying together — even one Hail Mary. Pray the Rosary with your children. Some Christians teach against the Rosary, thinking that our Lord is against repetition, but He is not. Jesus and His followers prayed the psalms, which are filled with repetition in praise of God. Psalm 136, for example, repeats in every other line, "His mercies are new every morning." Jesus condemned vain repetition. Meditating on the life of our Lord in the Rosary is not a vain endeavor.

Fourth, pray with humility and faith. This most beautiful quote from a Jewish sage sums it up well:

> *"It is proper for you to know, my brother, that the aim of our devotion in prayer consists in naught save the soul's longing for God, humbling itself before Him, and extolling the Creator with praise and gratitude unto His name, and casting all burdens upon Him" (Bahia ibn Pakkudah, Duties of the Heart, iii).*

RM

What "key" can I implement to improve immediately the quality of my prayer life?

IN CLOSING...

"There is no queen like humility to make the King surrender. Humility drew the King from heaven to the womb of the Virgin, and with it, by one hair, we will draw Him to our souls."

ST. TERESA OF AVILA

Lord, You know how often my pride keeps me from running after you. Forgive me, Lord, and give me grace to kneel close to Your heart. Amen.

Lesson Two

Vocal Prayer

Prayer: An Act of Love

O My God, I love Thee above all things,
with my whole heart and soul,
because Thou art all-good and worthy of all love.
I love my neighbor as myself for the love of Thee.
I forgive all who have injured me, and ask pardon
of all whom I have injured. Amen.

WEEKLY THEME

Supported by consistent prayer, my daily life will be transformed.

WEEKLY GRACE

I pray for the grace to have a regular, established time of prayer each day.

Full of Grace: Read pages 31 - 33 in the text, and then answer the following questions.

1. What are the two categories of vocal prayer? Describe each. What attitude of heart should we bring to vocal prayer?

____

____

____

2. How can we evaluate the quality of our vocal prayer?

____

____

____

3. What is *mental prayer?* What does it signify about the interior life?

____

____

____

4. List three practical strategies you can use to be more fervent in vocal prayer:

   a. ______________________________

   b. ______________________________

   c. ______________________________

KNOW THE FAITH

Vocal Prayer: An Expression of Love

In the section on prayer, The *Catechism of the Catholic Church* tells us that "prayer is the life of the new heart" and that it should "animate us at every moment" (No. 2697). Therefore, vocal prayer is meant to be much more than the mere recitation of words; it is meant to be an expression of our love for the God who has done great things for us.

Vocal prayer, like meditation and contemplation, requires an inner disposition that weds together the deepest part of our being to the words we speak. St. John Chrysostom reminds us of the necessity of praying from the heart. He says, "Whether or not our prayer is heard depends not on the number of words, but on the fervor of our souls." May our vocal prayer be a reflection of the interior fire of our soul ignited with love of God.

Read paragraphs 2701 to 2704 in the *Catechism,* which instruct us on how to increase the fervor of our vocal prayer. Then answer the questions below.

1. How did Jesus use vocal prayer?

____

____

____

____

2. Why must we use our senses in prayer? How does it satisfy a divine requirement, and how is it an initial form of contemplative prayer?

____

____

____

____

WORD TO KNOW

Litany: In her *Encyclopedia of Catholic Devotions and Practices,* Ann Ball describes a litany as "a prayer in the form of responsive petition. In Old Testament times, the Jews had a form of public prayer in which one or more persons would pronounce an invocation and those present would answer by repeating a certain prayer. The early Church retained this practice, calling these alternating prayers a litany, from the Greek litaneia, meaning 'a humble fervent appeal.' In the Latin Church, a typical structure developed gradually." The five litanies sanctioned for public use are: The Litany of Loretto (or Litany of the Blessed Virgin), The Litany of the Saints, The Litany of the Holy Name, The Litany of the Sacred Heart, and The Litany of St. Joseph.

FOR PONDERING...

Praying Loud and Clear

Some Catholic women love formulated vocal prayers. The familiar words allow us to lift our minds and hearts above petty daily concerns or obsessive worries to enter into the beautiful world of God's kingdom. Other women have unpleasant associations with this kind of prayer, and recall being forced to pray with family when they would rather have been doing almost anything else. For these women, learning that God is equally pleased with spontaneous personal words from the heart is liberating.

Praying in your own words, for even five minutes a day, is good for the soul. Just tell the Lord what is uppermost on your mind and heart. This kind of regular prayer can be surprisingly effective in helping us to break through into a different mansion of Our Father's kingdom, as Teresa of Avila taught her spiritual daughters.

As you pray in your own words, listen interiorly for God's quiet voice in your heart. Most spiritual directors teach that all types of vocal prayer, formulated or spontaneous, are good. Unless obliged by a community commitment, choose the manner of vocal prayer with which you are happiest. Some of us are very comfortable with a spontaneous prayer offered at any time of day — we simply talk out loud to God. Others feel far more at ease when we retire to a quiet spot and kneel down to pray in a more formal manner, with a prayer book or Rosary in hand. Both kinds of prayer are effective and appropriate.

Keep in mind that, even if we are more comfortable with one type of prayer, the Holy Spirit might lead us down a new path, especially when our usual mode of prayer seems stale and arid. Some of us resist a mode of prayer that others love, only to find it to be just what we need at a particular time in our lives.

A method some Catholics use to personalize formulated vocal prayer is to add your own name and circumstances to whatever prayer you are saying, such as "Thy kingdom come to me, Susan, on earth here in Ohio as it is in heaven," or "Pray for me, a sinner, now and at the hour of my death." Another favorite vocal method is to offer the short prayers known as "ejaculations" such as, "Jesus, I love you!" or "Holy God, I praise your name!"

RC

How do I imagine God responding to my prayer conversation with Him each day?

____

____

____

____

IN CLOSING...

"We must pray without tiring, for the salvation of mankind does not depend on material success ... Neither does it depend on arms and human industries, but on Jesus alone."

ST. FRANCES CABRINI

Holy Spirit, come into my heart. Bring new life to the ancient prayers I learned as a child, and inspire me to voice my innermost thoughts to the God who knows them all. Amen.

Lesson Three

Meditation

Prayer: An Act of Hope

O My God, relying on Thy almighty power
and infinite mercy and promises,
I hope to obtain pardon of my sins, the help of thy grace,
and life everlasting, through the merits of
Jesus Christ, my Lord and Redeemer. Amen

WEEKLY THEME

Supported by consistent prayer, my daily life will be transformed.

WEEKLY GRACE

I pray for the grace to have a regular, established time of prayer each day.

Full of Grace: Read pages 34 - 37 in the text, then answer the following questions.

1. What is meditation, according to the *Catechism of the Catholic Church*? What are the four faculties of the human person it involves?

2. What are the steps outlined in *Full of Grace* that we can use to meditate on Scripture in our time of prayer?

3. What questions can we ask ourselves to help us mine the rich treasure in a Scripture passage?

4. Using the steps you have outlined, turn in your Bible to Matthew 6 and meditate on verses 23 - 34. In the space provided below, write down any insights, reflections, or thoughts that came to you during this time.

KNOW THE FAITH

Where Did the Bible Come From?

The Bible is not a single book; in reality, it contains a library of literature spanning thousands of years and comprised of a variety of genres. The Bible is God's revelation for mankind and the basis of all Catholic belief. The proclamation of Sacred Scripture has been part of the Holy Sacrifice of the Mass since the earliest days of Christianity.

Written by human authors under the inspiration of the Holy Spirit, the Old Testament traces the history of salvation, from Creation to the covenant God made with the Israelites in preparation for the coming of the Messiah, to the prophets who heralded His coming. The New Testament consists of the four Gospels and certain inspired writings from apostolic times.

According to Church Tradition, Scripture contains at least two different "senses" or interpretations — the literal sense and the spiritual sense (cf. CCC 115-119). As we study the Scriptures, our own interpretations must be guided, indeed subject, to the teaching authority of the Church. Only then are we safeguarded against the error, confusion and conflict that can result from the misinterpretation of isolated Scripture passages.

Catholics will often hear other Christians say that the Bible alone contains all of Christian truth. This doctrine of *sola scriptura* was taught by Protestant reformers. While the Catholic Church affirms that Sacred Scripture teaches "firmly, faithfully and without error that truth which God wanted to put into the sacred writings for the sake of our salvation" (*Dei Verbum*, no. 11), the written Word of God is not the *only* source of teaching and guidance for God's people. Nowhere does the Bible teach this. What it does tell us, however, is to "stand firm and to "hold fast to the traditions you received…either by word or letter" (2 Thessalonians 2:15).

The key word here is *tradition.* A tradition is something that is passed on from one group to another, or handed down from one person to another. The Greek word for tradition *(paradosis)* is the word St. Paul uses to explain how he received the gospel of Jesus (1 Corinthians 15:3-4) and what he then passed on to the early Christian communities (1 Corinthians 11:23). Oral tradition, communication through word of mouth, was the main means of passing on the teachings of Jesus in the early Church since a written Gospel did not exist until at least 60 A.D.

Catholic apologists, who explain the teachings of the Church in light of Sacred Scripture and Sacred Tradition, remind us that Jesus came not to give us a book, but to establish His Kingdom, His Church. And it is through His Church that the "canon," the official list of inspired writings, was determined. The bishops and elders of the Church, under the inspiration and guidance of the Holy Spirit, discerned whether or not each manuscript was in agreement with the traditions they had received from the apostles. Once this canon was established, the bishops submitted themselves wholeheartedly to its truth; they protected, proclaimed, and taught these inspired teachings to those souls entrusted to them. This has been their call, mission, and holy office from then to the present day and for all time.

1. In your own words, explain the importance of both Scripture and Tradition for imparting wisdom and truth.

2. How does this understanding of the inspiration and development of Sacred Scripture deepen my appreciation of it and of the Church's guardianship of it?

___

___

___

___

WORD TO KNOW

Oratory: A place—usually private—set aside for prayer. Both lay and religious groups sometimes set up an oratory for their members. In the past, and in some places even now, kings and queens often had a personal oratory in their castles. There the monarch could pray, pouring out his or her heart, without being watched by the hundreds who lived within the castle. Today, many families throughout the world set aside a small area of the home for quiet, devotional prayer.

FOR PONDERING...

Meeting God in Meditation

Many Catholics claim to be too busy to read the Bible or other great spiritual literature. Usually this means that they have not discovered how enriching it is to meditate on the words that the Holy Spirit has inspired others to write down for our benefit. We might say, "Well I hear Scripture at Mass on Sunday. During the week I am too tired, I need to relax." Then, after chilling out in front of the TV or at the game board on the computer, we complain that we're stressed and tense and can hardly sleep!

Meditating on Scripture needs to be a regular part of your daily prayer time. During the dialogue we have with God that makes up our meditation, we may not "hear," even in the silence of our hearts, any distinct message from our beloved Lord. A holy sister, devoted to prayer, told me once that God spoke to her, not in words, but in silence. In a way, silence is the language of God. However, those led by this wordless path often see the truths of Scripture illustrated in daily life, in the beauty of a child's face or the roaring of the sea.

Sometimes God does seem to whisper a definitive message to our hearts. However, the Church teaches that we should never take such messages of private revelation to be infallible, especially if they urge action contrary to reason or tell us to spread concepts contrary to doctrine. Any such words must be taken to a competent spiritual director for discernment.

But that doesn't mean we must be "deaf" to whatever comes to us during meditative prayer. We have a right and even a duty to listen carefully to the inspirations given in prayer, especially because they bring light into the foggy darkness of our usual train of disgruntled, angry, or peevish conceptions about what is going on around us.

For example, if you were meditating on the Our Father, you might close your eyes and then hear God in your heart "saying" something like, "Dear little one, I am your Father who loves you. Have hope, all will be well." How encouraging!

If you have a busy day, a good time to meditate on the Bible or on other spiritual reading, is a short time just before going to sleep. Try this on a nightly basis for a while. Those who are learning how meaningful it is to take a real Sabbath on Sundays, will often include a time of meditation.

RC

Is there a small window of time that I've reserved for "myself" that I could spend in quiet meditation? What would this time be?

IN CLOSING...

"For perfected souls every place is to them an oratory; every moment a time of prayer."

ST. CATHERINE OF SIENNA

St. Augustine observed, "Thou has made us for Thyself, O God, and our hearts are restless until they rest in Thee." Jesus, you have promised to give rest to those who come to you. Have mercy on me and multiply my feeble efforts. Help me to not lose heart but persevere. Amen.

Lesson Four

Contemplation: The Divine Life Within

WEEKLY THEME
Supported by consistent prayer, my daily life will be transformed.

WEEKLY GRACE
I pray for the grace to have a regular, established time of prayer each day.

Prayer: An Act of Faith

O My God, I firmly believe
that Thou art one God in three Divine Persons,
Father, Son and Holy Spirit;
I believe that Thy Divine Son became man,
and died for our sins,
and that He will come to judge the living and the dead.
I believe these and all the truths that
the Holy Catholic Church teaches
because Thou hast reveal them,
Who canst neither deceive nor be deceived. Amen

Full of Grace: Read pages 37 - 42 and then answer the following questions.

1. In what three ways does contemplation differ from meditation?

   a. ______________________________

   b. ______________________________

   c. ______________________________

   According to Father Thomas Dubay, S.M., what one attribute of contemplation is the same for everyone?

   ____

   ____

2. What is "mystical union?"

   ____

   ____

   ____

3. Reread the quotation from *Introduction to Spirituality,* by Father Louis Bouyer. How does faith conform us to itself? What definition of contemplation is implicit in the quote?

   ____

   ____

4. What are three spiritual dangers in seeking the consolations of God rather than the God of consolation?

   a. ______________________________

   b. ______________________________

   c. ______________________________

KNOW THE FAITH

The Battle of Prayer

St. Teresa of Avila said, "It is essential to begin the practice of prayer with a firm resolution of persevering in it." Implicit in this statement are two virtues absolutely essential to growing in prayer and the spiritual life — discipline and perseverance.

The necessity of these two virtues indicates something more to us as well. Prayer is not always easy. It requires effort. Paragraphs 2725-28 in the *Catechism of the Catholic Church* tell us why this is so, and point out to us some of the major hindrances we may face. Look for the answers to the following questions as you read:

1. Who are the two enemies of prayer?

   a. ______________________________

   b. ______________________________

2. What are some *erroneous notions* about prayer? Ask yourself, "Have I ever held to any of them? If so, in what way?"

____

____

____

____

____

3. How can the *mentality* of "this present world" penetrate our life of prayer? Are any of these a challenge for me?

____

____

____

____

____

4. Which of the *failures* in prayer have I experienced in the past or am I now experiencing? What is the remedy?

WORD TO KNOW

Mysticism: An experiential knowledge of God's presence in which the soul has a sense of contact with Him. This knowledge need not be accompanied by any psycho-physical phenomena such as visions or ecstasies. Mystical experiences are spiritual gifts that God gives to whom He wills; authentic mysticism cannot be induced by an act of human will.

FOR PONDERING...

Intimacy with God Is Transformative

A woman came up to me one day after a Bible class. "Will you pray for my husband?" she asked, launching into a litany of complaints and problems that could only be solved, she insisted, if her husband underwent a radical change. She had been praying for years but so far had seen no change. "I don't know why God hasn't answered my prayer."

I tried to explain that God gave her husband free will. When we pray for someone, God can answer our prayer by sending graces or by sending people to speak to the person we are praying for. If the person still won't listen, God sometimes sends problems so that the person becomes desperate and cries out for help. However, if a person refuses to say "yes" to God, God never overrides that person's free will, no matter how hard we pray.

"You must learn to be happy even if your husband doesn't change."

The woman's expression told me that this was not what she wanted to hear. "But I can't be happy if my husband doesn't change."

"Maybe that is the problem. You have made your husband the source of your happiness. If God were first in your life, then no one could take away your joy. Take your eyes off your husband and put them on God. Let God be the source of your joy."

I have had similar conversations with a number of women. Each time the woman decided to make God the source of her joy, miracles happened. In some cases, the woman discovered that her husband didn't need all that much changing, after all. Other times, when the wife stopped trying to change her husband, he decided to change on his own. Even in the most difficult cases, God gave these women peace in their hearts.

Each time we intercede on behalf of another, asking God to change that person, we must remember an important spiritual principle: Prayer transforms the one who prays as often as it affects the one for whom the prayer is offered.

DO'L

Sometimes the best prayer to bring to God is "Lord, change me." In what area do I need to be transformed by God's action in me?

IN CLOSING...

"Not by... violence will [the Church] regain her beauty but through peace and through the constant and humble prayers and sweat and tears poured out by my servants with eager desire."

FROM THE WRITINGS OF ST. CATHERINE OF SIENA

Lord, let my life be a "living sacrifice" of praise. Give me grace to willingly offer up the slights and inconveniences that otherwise might rob me of joy. Teach me to recognize in every circumstance an opportunity to practice virtue and grow in faith. Amen.

Lesson Five

Effects of Prayer

Prayer: The Magnificat (Luke 1:49-50)

"The mighty God has done great things for me, and
Holy is His name.
His mercy reaches from age to age."

WEEKLY THEME
Supported by consistent prayer, my daily life will be transformed.

WEEKLY GRACE
I pray for the grace to have a regular, established time of prayer each day.

Full of Grace: Read pages 42 to 44, then answer the following questions.

1. What is the primary effect of prayer, and how is it seen?

2. In the story of the demoniac, at first the man was afraid to encounter Jesus. Ask yourself: "Have I ever been afraid of Jesus? Of what was I afraid?"

3. Sometimes we are reluctant to make necessary changes in our lives. We become comfortable with undesirable behaviors, and may even rationalize our sins. Have you ever experienced this in your life? Under what circumstances?

4. Jesus desires to heal us, transform us, and set us free. Ask yourself: "How can I cooperate with Him in the situation(s) I have listed above?"

KNOW THE FAITH

We never need to feel powerless over a particular weakness or fault. As the *Catechism* teaches, conversion of heart is God's work; if we ask Him to work in us, He is fully capable of renewing even the darkest and weakest recesses of our hearts.

Read Paragraphs 1430-32 in the *Catechism,* then answer the following questions.

1. How does interior conversion manifest itself? How have I seen this in my own life regarding a sin from which I have repented?

2. What does *animi cruciatus* and *compunctio cordis* mean? How does a penitent experience them?

3. What does "conversion" mean? (Hint: Reread Paragraph 1432.)

WORD TO KNOW

Compunction: This word comes from the Latin meaning "to puncture." Compunction is a "prick of the conscience;" a deep uneasiness of regret and sorrow; true remorse.

FOR PONDERING...

Banish Confusion

As you read through the story of the demoniac of Gerasenes, you may not identify with him. You don't spend time running around a cemetery half-clothed, screaming and howling, tormented by a legion of awful demons. You may, however, have one secret demon tormenting you, something you would like to change, have tried to change, but found that the problem keeps coming back to haunt you.

Looking around the *Woman of Grace®* group, you might think, "Everyone else here is so pulled together. If they really knew me, they would probably kick me out of the group!" But the truth is, most of us have, or have had, secret demons tormenting us.

The Good News is that Jesus came to set us free from all oppression. For some of us, the change we experience will be as dramatic as it was for the demoniac; for others, only their confessor will know the profound nature of their transformation in Christ.

If you have a secret problem and you want to be free, start by going to confession. If you have already confessed this problem and nothing has changed, don't despair. Keep going back. You may be ashamed to go back and confess the same thing, but persevere. Tell Jesus that you really want to be free.

I had such a secret torment. I went to confession every week or so and confessed the same failure for over a year. It seemed the more I went to confession, the more often I failed. I couldn't understand why didn't Jesus immediately set me free! The truth was that although I didn't like the consequences of my problem, I didn't really want to change. It was as if I were sitting too close to a fire and the only way Jesus could get me to move was to make the fire hotter.

The situation continued to deteriorate, until finally I decided that I had had enough. I was ready to let go. Then while I was in prayer, I suddenly saw the error in my thinking that was at the root of the problem. From that moment, I was free from the torment. Only then was I able to be the person God wanted me to be—at least in that area of my life.

DO'L

Ask yourself: "Is there a secret sin that I am harboring in my life?" If the answer is yes, ask the Lord to help you think of three practical ways to overcome it.

____

____

____

____

IN CLOSING...

"God... does not desire the death of a sinner, but magnanimously awaits his return to Him."

ST. MARY OF EGYPT

Try as I might, Lord, I can never hide from Your all-seeing eyes. Nor should I want to, for You alone can bring healing and wholeness to the broken places of my life. Give me courage, God, to trust Your mercy. Amen.

Chapter Three

Praise and Thanksgiving, Petition and Contrition: Symphony of the Abundant Life

Full of Grace: This week covers pages 45-78 of the text.

Women of Grace are women of prayer. That prayer might be as simple as a child's shout of joy at the sight of a rainbow, or as deep as a whispered act of contrition motivated by true sorrow. Prayer is our first recourse when the world abandons us, the song of the human heart to the Divine Lover. Prayer is the constant counsel of the Blessed Virgin, the saints and the angels. And yet... there are times we are not sure how we ought to pray.

In this chapter you will learn the four types of prayer that Jesus taught His disciples, as well as how and when to employ each of them. You will also examine any personal obstacles to a more complete prayer life. This is important because a healthy prayer life is the lifeline for women charged with "saving humanity," as Pope John Paul II exhorts modern women to do.

LESSON ONE — Four Movements of Prayer
LESSON TWO — Praise the Lord, O My Soul
LESSON THREE — Thanksgiving, The Song of a Grateful Heart
LESSON FOUR — Petition, The Cry of Our Hearts
LESSON FIVE — Contrition, The Right Attitude to Bring to Prayer

Questions to Ponder This Week

- Who is God, and how may I know Him? And who am I, that He delights in my prayer?
- There is no sin or human frailty greater than God's mercy. How does this truth set me free?

Media Response Sheet

Praise and Petition, Thanksgiving and Contrition: Symphony of the Abundant Life

WEEKLY THEME

Our prayer life can help us, as Daughters of God, to renew the face of the earth.

WEEKLY GRACE

I pray for the grace to grow in fervency and dedication to prayer.

Answer the following questions as you watch the pre-recorded lesson given by Johnnette S. Benkovic, founder of Women of Grace®.

1. What are the "Dreaded D's" of prayer?

 a. ______________________________

 b. ______________________________

 c. ______________________________

2. What three virtues do the Three D's lead us in?

 a. ______________________________

 b. ______________________________

 c. ______________________________

3. What are the four movements in our symphony of prayer, which correspond to the word ACTS?

 a. ______________________________

 b. ______________________________

 c. ______________________________

4. God doesn't need our praises, but we need to praise Him. Why?

____

____

____

____

____

5. What are the five ways to cultivate the virtue of gratitude?

a. ______________________________

b. ______________________________

c. ______________________________

d. ______________________________

e. ______________________________

6. What was it the Canaanite woman did that made her prayer so effective?

a. ______________________________

b. ______________________________

c. ______________________________

7. According to St. Thomas Aquinas, how does God incorporate our prayers into His plans?

____

____

____

____

____

8. Why does God seem to delay in answering our prayers?

a. ______________________________

b. ______________________________

c. ______________________________

9. The *Catechism of the Catholic Church* tells us that true sorrow for our sins is a prerequisite for ______________ ______________ because ______________ ______________ brings us back into communion with God and His Son, Jesus Christ.

10. What sin is greater than God's mercy?

____

____

Woman of Grace

St. Scholastica (480 – 543)

St. Gregory the Great recounts this story from the life of St. Benedict's beloved twin sister, St. Scholastica, which shows how expressing our petitions to God with childlike faith and confidence sometimes yields immediate and amazing results.

After Benedict founded a monastery for men, Scholastica remained very close to her brother, founding a convent for women some miles away. Every year Scholastica went to visit Benedict at a little place just outside the monastery gate.

During one of these annual visits, the two spent the day together, along with a few members of their communities, praising God and talking about sacred things. They had supper and their conversation wore on late into the night. Finally Scholastica entreated her brother to stay with her overnight, so they could continue to talk about the delights of the spiritual life. But Benedict refused, saying he could not stay outside of his cell.

Disappointed but undaunted, Scholastica clasped her hands together, laid her head on them, and began to pray. As she lifted her head, the sky lit up with brilliant flashes of lightning. Thunder clapped and sheets of rain descended from the heavens. So heavy was the downpour that Benedict and his disciples could not leave.

Benedict was not pleased. Turning to his sister, he complained, "May God forgive you, sister. What have you done?"

Nonplussed, Scholastica answered, "Well, I asked you and you would not listen; so I asked my God and he did listen. So now go off, if you can, leave me and return to your monastery."

Benedict had little choice but to stay with his sister, and they passed the night talking about the spiritual life. Three days later, as St. Benedict looked out of his cell, he saw a dove flying into the heavens, and knew instantly that the soul of his sister was leaving her body and going to the place God had prepared for her from all eternity. He rejoiced in the great glory of his sister and thanked God with hymns and words of praise.

St. Benedict sent his disciples to bring Scholastica's body back to the monastery, and he laid her to rest in the tomb he had prepared for himself. St. Gregory wrote, "*Their minds had always been united in God; their bodies were to share a common grave.*" In granting Scholastica's heartfelt petition of love, He permitted brother and sister to spend one last visit together in His holy name.

St. Gregory the Great concludes the story by commenting on Scholastica's prayer: "*Contrary to what Benedict wanted, he found that a miracle was worked by the courage of one woman in the strength of God. No wonder the woman was more powerful than he; she had long desired to see her brother. As St. John said, 'God is love.' So with good reason she was more powerful who loved more.*"

FAITH IN ACTION

St. Scholastica's petition to God was motivated by her deep love for Benedict and her desire to spend more time with her brother. What are three of my most recent petitions to God? To what extent are they motivated by selfless love versus selfish wants?

Woman of Grace

Bl. Mary of Christ Crucified (Mariam Baouardy, the "Little Arab," 1846-1878)

Mariam Baouardy is a living example of how God uses even great evil for greater good. Her Syrian parents, who had previously lost twelve sons in infancy, believed that God would hear their prayer and bless them with a child. To this end, they made a trip to Bethlehem to beseech the Mother of God for the favor of a daughter. On the eve of the Epiphany, January 5, 1846, their daughter was born, and they named her "Mariam" in honor of the Virgin Mary. Two years later they had a baby boy, Boulos (Paul).

Early in Mariam's childhood, her parents died and an uncle adopted her; another relative adopted her little brother. Shortly thereafter Mariam's new family relocated to Alexandria, Egypt, where at age thirteen she was given in marriage to a man she had never met. Filled with anxiety, Miriam spent the night before the wedding ceremony in prayer before an icon of the Blessed Mother, begging for guidance and consolation. Deep in her heart, Jesus said to her, "Everything passes! If you wish to give me your heart, I will remain with you." A little later, again she heard Him speak. "Mariam, I am with you; follow the inspiration I shall give you. I will help you."

The next morning, Mariam refused to marry the man chosen for her. Furious, the uncle made Mariam a servant of the family, and gave her the lowliest of duties. Suffering greatly, Mariam finally wrote a letter to her brother, seeking his help, and asked a Muslim domestic who worked in her uncle's house to deliver the letter for her. The servant encouraged Mariam to share her troubles with him, hoping to convert her to Islam. When Mariam refused, staunchly declaring herself a "daughter of the Church," the Muslim domestic drew his sword and slashed her throat, then dumped Mariam's limp and bloodied body in an alley. It was September 8, 1858, the Feast of the Nativity of Mary.

Years later, Mariam related what happened next: "A nun dressed in blue picked me up and stitched my throat wound.... I found myself in heaven with the Blessed Virgin, the angels and the saints. They treated me with great kindness. In their company were my parents. I saw the brilliant throne of the Most Holy Trinity and Jesus Christ in His humanity. There was no sun, no lamp, but everything was bright with light. Someone spoke to me, saying that I was a virgin but that my book was not finished.

"When my wound was healed I had to leave the grotto, and the Lady took me to the Church of St. Catherine, served by the Franciscan Friars." Mariam never returned to her uncle's house. She worked as a domestic, and entered Carmel at the age of twenty-one, taking the name Sister Mary of Jesus Crucified.

Before she died at the age of thirty-three, Mariam was favored with many supernatural manifestations that caused her great suffering including the stigmata, knowledge of hearts, and facial radiance. Throughout all of these she clung, childlike, to her faith in Jesus Christ and His Blessed Mother. Pope John Paul II beatified her in 1983, and today she is known throughout Palestine as "Al Qiddisa" (the holy one). Despite her great sufferings, or perhaps because of them, she wrote:

> *"The whole world is asleep, and God so full of goodness, so great, so worthy of all praise, no one is thinking of Him! See, nature praises Him, and man...who ought to praise Him, sleeps! Let us go, let us go and wake up the universe...and sing His praises."*

FAITH IN ACTION

What praiseworthy dimension of God will I try to remember each day?

Lesson One

Four Movements of Prayer

Prayer of St. Gertrude the Great

O eternal sweetness of my soul, Thou who alone art the Beloved of my heart, Thy face is all lovely and Thy Heart all inviting; but my thoughts, alas! go wandering far from Thee. Come, O God of my heart, gather together my scattered mental powers and fix them upon Thyself.

WEEKLY THEME

Our prayer life can help us, as Daughters of God, to renew the face of the earth.

WEEKLY GRACE

I pray for the grace to grow in fervency and dedication to prayer.

Full of Grace: Read pages 45 to 48 in the text, then answer the following questions.

1. Briefly describe each "prayer of ACTS."

   a. __________

   b. __________

   c. __________

   d. __________

2. Which of these types of prayer come most naturally to you, and why?

3. Which of these types of prayer is most difficult for you, and why?

4. Based on today's text, how does the presence of prayerful women serve as a conduit of God's love in the world?

___

___

___

___

KNOW THE FAITH

The Liturgy of the Hours (Divine Office)

The Liturgy of the Hours is the cycle of the Church's daily prayer, used to sanctify the day. The Office of Readings consists of morning prayer, daytime prayers, evening prayer, and night prayer. According to the Church, morning prayer and evening prayer are the two "hinges" of the Liturgy of the Hours, and should be celebrated as such (see the "Constitution on the Sacred Liturgy," no. 89).

Prior to the Second Vatican Council, the Divine Office consisted of Matins, Lauds, Prime, Terce, Sext, None, Vespers, and Compline. Although the Council Fathers revised both the name and form of this ancient liturgy "*so that it could more fittingly be used by the clergy and other members of the Church in the circumstances of modern life*"(CSL, no. 81), some still refer to the Liturgy of the Hours by its original name.

Central to the Liturgy of the Hours are psalms, scripture passages, canticles, hymns, writings from the Church Fathers and the saints, and prayers. These writings are arranged to coincide with the Church calendar and with feast days. All 150 psalms are presented in a four-week cycle.

The origins of the Liturgy of the Hours can be traced back to the earliest days of the Church. Like their Jewish contemporaries and predecessors, the early Christian community gathered at designated times of the day to read Scripture and pray the Psalms. Because of Roman persecution, however, both the times and the number of prayers had to be flexible.

When the persecution of the Christians ended with Constantine, the Liturgy of the Hours became more standardized. Priests, deacons, acolytes, and laity would gather together with the local bishop in the cathedral to sing morning and evening prayer. In this way, they sought to obey the instruction of St. Paul to pray without ceasing. The *Apostolic Constitutions,* a Church document written in 380, states, "*Assemble yourselves every day, morning and evening, singing psalms and praying in the Lord's house.*"

The advent of monasticism brought further development to the Divine Office. Lay people who desired a deeper union with God began to flock to the desert to be totally dedicated to prayer. In time, they gathered in monastic communities, where they sang or recited the Psalms for morning and evening prayer. Gradually these communities expanded their time of communal prayer, and the "Hours" was born. The Hours were adopted by some of the cathedrals in the cities. Though laity continued to participate in morning and evening prayer, over time the Divine Office came to be observed almost exclusively by priests and religious, reading from Latin breviaries.

With the Liturgical Movement at the turn of the twentieth century, the Hours once again found their way back into the prayer life of the lay faithful. This movement sought to put the liturgy back into the lives of the laity and to teach them how to enter more deeply into the liturgical life of the Church. Pope Pius X gave this movement his official approval in 1903. Soon after, many lay people began to pray the Office and to experience the sense of unity with the whole Church that it brings.

The Second Vatican Council furthered the work of the Liturgical Movement, reminding the faithful that they belong to all the People of God. In the "Constitution on the Sacred Liturgy," the Second Vatican Council fathers state that the Liturgy of the Hours "is a source of piety and nourishment for personal prayer, and all who participate in it are earnestly exhorted in the Lord to attune their minds to their voices when praying it" (par. 90). Today, many Catholic parishes offer communal morning prayer after the morning Mass.

1. How does the Liturgy of the Hours connect us with the universal Church?

____

____

____

2. In addition to this connection, how do you think participating in these daily prayers help a layperson to live out her vocation more fully?

____

____

____

WORD TO KNOW

Liturgy: This Greek word refers to a public duty or work. The official and public worship of the Church including the prayers, rites, and ceremonies of the Church principally the Holy Sacrifice of the Mass, the sacraments, and the Liturgy of the Hours.

FOR PONDERING...

Reflection: Multiply Time

Many busy women think that they don't have time to pray. Their days are crowded with laundry, shopping, working, cleaning, chauffeuring the kids, and helping family and friends. They get up tired and go to bed tired. Suggest to them that they fit 15 minutes into their schedule for God (let alone an hour) and they will explain that they simply don't have an extra 15 minutes.

The problem is, they don't understand that God can multiply time, just as He multiplied the loaves and the fishes. Humanly speaking, a few loaves and fishes could never feed thousands of people — but God did it. Humanly speaking, we are each given the same twenty-four hours and seven days each week — but God holds each moment in His hands. He takes the time we give Him, and gives it back tenfold.

I have never seen it fail. When I set aside time for prayer, there is time for everything else; when I neglect my prayer time, the rest of the day is chaos. I find myself hunting for misplaced items and being late for appointments, getting lost, going to the store only to find they don't have what I want, wasting time waiting in line or stuck in traffic. The time just slips away and I end the day not having spent time with God *and* not having accomplished the things I thought were more important than spending time in prayer.

A number of years ago after all my children were in school, I went to a priest for spiritual direction. He asked me if I went to daily Mass. I said, "No."

"Can you go to daily Mass?" he asked. I had to admit that I could, I had a car and the church and the time were convenient.

"Do you think that Jesus wants you to go to daily Mass?" the priest probed.

When he put it like that, I knew he was right. I started to go to daily Mass. In the years since, I have kept up the practice. I start each day by deciding when and where I am going to Mass. No matter where I am while traveling, I find a Mass. For those who can't get to daily Mass, the Mass is shown on EWTN several times each day. And those who don't get EWTN can get a daily missal and pray the prayers of the Mass.

When we put God first, everything else will fall into place. Remember, whatever you need, give that to God and He will multiply it.

DO'L

Look up the Mass times of churches in your area and write them down. Is it possible you could add one additional Mass per week to your weekday schedule? Pray about it.

____

____

____

____

____

____

IN CLOSING...

"To establish Himself in the innermost of souls, such is God's desire. God's need, granted the charity of His Being, is avid to communicate what He is, infinite Love. He wants to possess souls, not only through His ordinary presence... but according to a wish of love on the part of the creature, in order to render him happy. Therein is the sole ambition of God: to transform us into His Unity."

FROM THE DIARY OF VENERABLE CONCHITA
(Concepcion Cabrera de Armida)

Jesus, You took a boy's lunch and fed the hungry crowds who came to hear You speak. Take the moments of my day that I offer You now, and fill my heart with Your Presence. Not for my own sake, but that I might carry You into the world wherever I go. Amen.

Lesson Two

Praise the Lord, O My Soul

Prayer from Psalm 63:3-5
"My lips will speak your praise,
so I will bless you all my life,
in your name I will lift up my hands.
My soul shall be filled as with a banquet,
my mouth shall praise you with joy."

WEEKLY THEME
Our prayer life can help us, as Daughters of God, to renew the face of the earth.

WEEKLY GRACE
I pray for the grace to grow in fervency and dedication to prayer.

Full of Grace: Read pages 48 to 54, and then answer the following questions.

1. Why do we praise and adore God? Why isn't thanking him the same thing?

2. What are three ways we can incorporate praise into our daily life?

3. What is it about praising God in the midst of a trial that is so transforming?

4. Write your own prayer of praise and adoration, expressing your love of God.

KNOW THE FAITH

The History of the Psalms

The Book of Psalms is one book of Sacred Scripture that seems to express every human emotion. From the depths of despair to the heights of jubilation, from anger and revenge to repentance and remorse, from fear and distrust to courage and confidence, the Psalms mirror the human condition.

The word *psalm* means "a poem to be sung." About half of the one hundred fifty psalms are attributed to David, the rest being attributed to Moses, Solomon or any one of five other minor sources. These sacred poems became the hymnbook of Israel and subsequently of the Catholic Church.

Many of the psalms are hymns of praise and adoration; they proclaim God's power and might, the glory of His creation, God's fidelity to His chosen people, His goodness and mercy. Other psalms are songs of thanksgiving that express gratitude to God for his liberation from personal danger or national disaster. Still others petition God for protection from imminent peril, calamity, and the evil of others. Of the one hundred fifty psalms, seven of them are penitential psalms, begging God for His pardon and forgiveness. Psalms 2, 72, 110 and 132 have clear Messianic themes, while all of the psalms express the hope of the Jew to be upheld by the providence of God.

Praying the Psalms according to the tradition of *lectio divina* helps us mine the rich treasure of these hymns, leading us into a closer relationship with God. To enter into the heart of the Psalms, we approach them on three levels:

1. The *historical,* human level: How is the psalm a response to the contemporary world of the psalmist, with all of its challenges and joys? Here, knowledge of Jewish history helps place the psalm in its proper context.
2. The *Christian* level: How does Jesus Christ fulfill the longings of the Jewish people expressed in the psalm?
3. The *personal* level: How does this psalm relate to your own life or express the cry of your heart, whether it be joyful, sorrowful, hopeful, penitent, or wanting?

Psalms has been a mainstay of Christian spirituality since its beginning days. They are used in public worship in the Holy Sacrifice of the Mass and the Liturgy of the Hours, and have formed a part of private devotion for millennia.

Because many of the psalms refer to names and places of the Old Testament, our appreciation for the Book of Psalms will be enhanced as we familiarize ourselves with the history and geography of that time, and see God's interaction with His people in that day and age.

1. In my own life, how has a particular psalm expressed the emotions of my heart? What was it, and how did it do that?

2. Read Psalm 139 according to the three levels described above. Record your thoughts, insights, and any consolations you received.

WORD TO KNOW

Lectio Divina: A Latin expression meaning "sacred reading." Lectio divina includes four steps, which help a person move from simple meditation to true contemplation. These steps are: reading prayerfully, meditating on what has been read, yielding to the grace of God, formulating a response back to God in light of His movement of grace.

FOR PONDERING...

Reflection: All Glory, Laud, and Honor

How is praise and adoration different from thanksgiving? In *Full of Grace*, praise is described as lauding God not only for what He has done for each of us personally but also for His own glory.

It can help one to understand this religious practice better when you consider the way some philosophers explain the glory and praise. The Christian theologian Rudolf Otto, author of *The Idea of the Holy*, claims that the mysterious, fascinating, awesome, and captivating sense of the divine is in some form the universal experience of all people. The "Holy, Holy, Holy" of the angels is our way of expressing the sacredness of God's divinity.

C.S. Lewis thought that an experience of the divine provides the basis for accepting more formal proofs for God's existence. Catholic philosopher Dietrich Von Hildebrand spoke of the "obligation of due response" to whatever is beautiful, good, or holy.

Here is a simple example of due response. Suppose you paid the fare of a friend to meet you at Niagara Falls for a vacation. Upon your friend's arrival, how would you feel if he or she preferred spending the time in the motel, watching television, to seeing the Falls? The natural wonder would not suffer for it, but you would feel terribly upset. This is because delight in the magnificent cascade is the due response to its beauty. Even more so does God—who is absolute beauty, goodness, and truth—deserve our praise and adoration.

In *Full of Grace* we read about praising God even for negative circumstances. In terms of due response, praising of God even in times of great sadness is the due response to the providential love He has for us. We can count on that love always to bring something good out of the most difficult moments of our lives.

RC

It takes faith and trust to praise God for something painful in your life. Grace-filled women look expectantly to God, their heavenly Father, to bring good out of an illness, a job loss, even a broken relationship or the loss of a loved one. Have you had such an experience? Describe how praising God despite your pain changed your view of suffering.

IN CLOSING...

"Happy the enamored heart, thought centered on God alone,
Renouncing every creature for Him, finding in Him glory and contentment.
Living forgetful of self, in God is all its intention,
Happy and so joyfully it journeys through waves of this stormy sea..."

ST. TERESA OF AVILA

Great God of wonders, all Your ways are full of matchless glory. All creation whispers of the unfathomable beauty and splendor that is to come. Let all the nations praise You, for You are worthy of all praise! Amen.

Lesson Three

Thanksgiving, the Song of a Grateful Heart

WEEKLY THEME
Our prayer life can help us, as Daughters of God, to renew the face of the earth.

WEEKLY GRACE
I pray for the grace to grow in fervency and dedication to prayer.

Prayer: Psalm 40

I waited patiently for the Lord;
He inclined to me and heard my cry.
He drew me up from the desolate pit,
out of the miry bog,
and set my feet upon a rock,
making my steps secure.
He put a new song in my mouth,
a song of praise to our God.
Many will see and fear,
and put their trust in the Lord. Amen.

Full of Grace: Read pages 55 - 59 in the text, then answer the following questions.

1. Can you think of a time you received the heartfelt gratitude of someone close to you? How did it make you feel? Is there something in your own life now that you need to thank God for with great fervor?

____

____

____

2. What are three effects of cultivating a spirit of gratitude? Briefly explain each.

a. ______________________________

b. ______________________________

c. ______________________________

3. Humility is one of the most difficult virtues. It begins when we acknowledge that we are not the center of the world around us, but an important part of a whole. Name three ways you can demonstrate your gratitude to God by aiding others with the particular graces God has given *you*.

a. ______________________________

b. ______________________________

c. ______________________________

4. What are the five ways to cultivate a spirit of gratitude? Which one of these ways do I most need to practice and why?

a. ______________________________

b. ______________________________

c. ______________________________

d. ______________________________

e. ______________________________

KNOW THE FAITH

Thanksgiving – A Tradition from the Beginning

Offering thanks to God is as old as humanity itself. The following passage has been adapted from *Handbook of Christian Feasts and Customs,* written by Francis X. Weiser. Read it, and then answer the following questions.

1. What commonalities do you see between the way the Jews of the Old Testament offered thanksgiving to God and the Holy Sacrifice of the Mass?

____

____

____

2. According to this selection, why is every day of the year "Thanksgiving Day" in the Catholic Church and how do I seek to enter into this "attitude of gratitude?"

____

____

____

3. What significant events or situations in my lifetime have led to a special Mass of thanksgiving being celebrated? What was my interior response at this Mass?

____

____

____

From the very beginning, human beings have instinctively offered thanks to God for His many gifts to them. Thanksgiving is one of four human motivations for divine worship, along with adoration, contrition, and supplication.

We find archeological and anthropological evidence of rites of sacrifice and thanksgiving since the dawn of human history. Under the Old Covenant, the Jews offered sacrifices to God, both individually and as a community, as proscribed in the Law of Moses (see Leviticus 1-3 and 7). There were many kinds of gifts, predominately various clean animals (or animal blood) and grain or bread.

This offering continues in a unique way under the New Covenant, especially in the Sacrifice of the Mass. The four movements of worship—adoration and contrition, thanksgiving and petition—are perpetuated here. The very word Eucharist, derived from the Greek word for "thanksgiving," points to the fact that from the earliest times the Christian community recognized the Liturgy of the Eucharist as the greatest act of thanksgiving that could be offered to God. As Father Weiser observes, "In the Catholic Church, liturgically speaking, every day of the year is 'Thanksgiving Day.'"

Of course, in every community and culture there have been times when people wished to offer God thanksgiving in a deeper, more profound way. In the wake of sickness, famine, or war, survivors have sometimes sought to express their gratitude to the God who saved them. At such times, a Mass of thanksgiving is celebrated with increased splendor and fervency, and concluded with the recitation of the Te Deum Laudamus (God, We Praise Thee), a fourth-century hymn of praise.

WORD TO KNOW

Eucharist: From the Greek, eucharistia, meaning to give thanks or to grant a favor. In Catholic theology, the Eucharist is the sacrament instituted by Christ at the Last Supper (see Mt 26: 26-28, Mk 14: 22-24, Lk 22: 19-20, 1 Cor 11: 23-25). Jesus Christ is wholly, completely, and substantially present in the Eucharist: Body and Blood, Soul and Divinity.

FOR PONDERING...

Sing a New Song Unto the Lord

Cynics claim that whenever someone's actions appear to be good, there are always underlying selfish motives. Kind words, for example, might be false flattery to accrue favors. A gesture of kindness might be extended simply for self-gratification and self-promotion.

Of course, sometimes cynics are right. There are plenty of circumstances where people who appear to be doing good, actually have bad motives. However, such cynicism leaves no room for gratitude. Think about the millions of sacrifices parents make for their children. How sad it would be if an adult child had no gratitude, but chose instead to focus on her parents' shortcomings.

A Catholic philosopher, Balduin V. Schwarz, wrote extensively about thanksgiving. He noted that, if a kind act or good deed could be called a "gift," then the gratitude of the recipient, in a sense, "opens" the gift. To expand the image, unopened gifts collect dust. Without gratitude, not only does the recipient fail to enjoy the gift, he or she also fails to experience the personal love conveyed with the gift. If a child grabs a gift and never says thank you, he may enjoy the gift but he will not truly receive the love the donor wanted so much for the child to feel, as well.

In a like manner, how disappointed God is when His many gifts to us are ignored. He understands that we have difficulty believing He loves us when we have to carry terrible crosses, but what of our failure to see the love He pours out on us in the gift of life and every blessing that comes with it? I imagine God, as it were, looking over all the blessings He wants for us each day from a wayside flower to the Real Presence of His Son's Body and Blood in Holy Communion. "Surely these gifts will bring joy to the heart of my dear child," He might think. But how many Communions with the Lord have I missed because I was too laden down with worries? I received the Eucharist, but was too distracted to even make a thanksgiving.

Here is one simple way to increase awareness of all the good gifts of each day. This week carry around a little file card and jot down the joyful, luminous, sorrowful, and glorious mysteries in your life for each day. This serves as a way to personally echo the mysteries of Mary's life as expressed in the Rosary.

Try to find the joyful and glorious events and interior experiences of each day—especially if you are feeling the burden of heavy crosses. This will bring balance and opportunities for thanksgiving as you review your list at the end of the day.

RC

Sometimes God's gifts come wrapped in the dark shadows of suffering. However, even then there are blessings of grace inside. When and how have I learned this lesson?

IN CLOSING...

"I have given everything to my Master: He will take care of me... The best thing for us is not what we consider best, but what the Lord wants of us!"

SISTER JOSEPHINE BAKHITA

Dear Lord, thank You, thank You, thank You...! Today I want to cultivate a spirit of thanksgiving. Help me to see Your hand in even the ordinary circumstances of life. Amen.

Lesson Four

Petition, the Cry of Our Hearts

Prayer from the Liturgy of the Hours

God, come to my assistance.
Lord, make haste to help me.
Glory to the Father, and to the Son,
And to the Holy Spirit:
As it was in the beginning, is now,
And will be forever.
Amen. Alleluia.

WEEKLY THEME

Our prayer life can help us, as Daughters of God, to renew the face of the earth.

WEEKLY GRACE

I pray for the grace to grow in fervency and dedication to prayer.

Full of Grace: Read pages 60 - 68 in the text, and then answer the following questions.

1. What are the three attributes of prayer exhibited by the Canaanite woman? Which of these do I most need to acquire, and why?

   a. ______________________________

   b. ______________________________

   c. ______________________________

2. Read Mark 5: 25-34. This passage relates the story of the woman with the hemorrhage. How does she exhibit the same three attributes as the Canaanite woman?

   ____

   ____

   ____

   ____

3. Think of another example from Sacred Scripture where a person exhibits these characteristics and tell how he/she demonstrates the same qualities of prayer.

   ____

   ____

   ____

   ____

   ____

4. Think of one intention you have offered to God, for which you are still waiting an answer. What might be the cause of the delay?

____

____

____

____

____

KNOW THE FAITH

Confident and Faith-Filled Prayer

Paragraph 2739 in the *Catechism of the Catholic Church* tells us that we do not pray alone before the Father. Jesus prays with us — "in our place and on our behalf." Read the rest of this paragraph. Then read paragraphs 2742 to 2745, and answer the questions that follow.

The knowledge that we are not alone in our intercessions should give us the courage to pray with faith, confidence, and perseverance. If we grow weary of making our petitions known to the Father through the Son, we must resist the impulse to quit. Prayer can be a battle, but we must persevere in love.

1. What are the three life-giving facts of faith about prayer?

   a. ______________________________

   b. ______________________________

   c. ______________________________

2. Based on Paragraph 2743, what are some less-obvious opportunities I have to pray, given my specific daily activities and responsibilities?

____

____

____

____

3. Name three reasons why prayer and the Christian life are inseparable.

   a. ______________________________

   b. ______________________________

   c. ______________________________

WORD TO KNOW

Providence: When this word refers to God, it means the way that God, in His infinite wisdom, orders all events in the universe so that the end for which all things were created may be realized: That end is to manifest the glory of our Creator. We do this through serving God in obedience and love, which ultimately leads to our own eternal happiness.

FOR PONDERING...

Let Your Requests Be Known

I remember once asking my elderly father to pray for a certain small intention. He replied, "I don't like to bother God with small things. I just wait until I really need something big."

Gently I reasoned with him. "Dad, God doesn't limit the number of prayers He answers. Look at it this way: Every time I come over, you ask me to bring some small thing you need or to take you somewhere. When you need something really important, will I say, 'Sorry, you're over your quota'? Of course not — and neither will God. He loves you much more than I do."

My father smiled.

We need to practice the prayer of petition on a daily basis. It is like using "please" at the dinner table. Just as "Please pass the potatoes" is a simple courtesy, so our prayers of petition remind us that all good gifts come from God. Just as we teach our children not to reach and grab, so we need to teach them to ask God for everything they need.

Some people think that it's silly to pray for material things — that you should pray only for "spiritual" things. But Jesus constantly stresses the importance of trusting God for *all* our material needs. When He sent the apostles out on a mission, He told them: "Do not take gold or silver or copper for your belts, no sack for the journey or second tunic or sandals or walking stick."

Why? He wanted them to learn to be totally dependent on God. Jesus knew that if they walked into a town tired, hungry, and penniless, their faith would increase each time they were housed and fed.

It worked. They came back praising God for the miracles that had happened.

If we practice asking God for everything we need, our faith will grow in the same way.

DO'L

Some women admit they are hesitant to pray for their own needs. Some have a sense of unworthiness; others worry that unanswered prayer will damage their fragile faith. Review the common misconceptions and misunderstandings listed on pages 62 – 63. Is there any reason that you've hesitated to offer prayers of petition on your own behalf?

____

____

____

____

IN CLOSING...

"God asks us to mortify ourselves in small things rather than in big ones because the big occasions are rare, whereas the small ones are continuous."

VENERABLE TERESA VALSE PANTELLINI

Lord, grant me the grace to recognize Your presence in my darkest moments, the courage to trust You in good times and bad, and the wisdom and compassion I need to share Your love with the world. Amen.

Lesson Five

Contrition, the Right Attitude to Bring to Prayer

Prayer: An Act of Contrition

O my God, I am heartily sorry for having offended Thee,
and I detest all my sins because of Thy just punishments,
but most of all because I have offended Thee my God,
Who art all good and deserving of all my love.
I firmly resolve, with the help of Thy grace, to sin no more,
and to avoid the near occasion of sin. Amen.

WEEKLY THEME

Our prayer life can help us, as Daughters of God, to renew the face of the earth.

WEEKLY GRACE

I pray for the grace to grow in fervency and dedication to prayer.

Full of Grace: Read pages 68–78 in the text, and then answer the following questions.

1. Name the two standards of St. Ignatius of Loyola and explain each.

2. Johnnette says each of us, like the Prodigal Son, "squanders" the gift of redemption through sin. Which of the failings listed in this section apply to me? What is its remedy? Will I do it?

3. Name the characteristics of a true conversion of heart.

4. Why do you think it is that great sinners so often become great saints?

____

____

____

____

KNOW THE FAITH

Whose Sins You Shall Forgive, They Are Forgiven

The Sacrament of Penance, sometimes called the Sacrament of Reconciliation, is one of Jesus' greatest gifts to His Church. Many contemporary Catholics do not use this gift regularly, and yet confessing our sins to a priest at least once a month is a good spiritual practice. A good confession—with sincerity of heart, sorrow for sin, a firm purpose to sin no more, full confession to a priest, and satisfaction for our sins through penance— helps us stay rooted in the life of faith, and helps us to make progress on the path of perfection.

The *Catechism of the Catholic Church* tells us that Christ gave this sacrament to all those who, after baptism, fall into grave sin. Such sin is considered "mortal" because it causes us to lose our baptismal grace, and wounds "ecclesial communion." However, Penance offers the possibility to recover that state of justified grace through continued conversion and renewal. The Fathers of the Church considered this sacrament "the second plank [of salvation] after the shipwreck, which is the loss of grace" (No. 1446).

Sometimes people object to the idea that one must confess sins to a priest. "Why can't I just tell God I'm sorry?" they ask. The Catholic Church teaches that only God can forgive sin. "Christ has willed that in her prayer and life and action His whole Church is used to be the sign and instrument of the forgiveness and reconciliation that He acquired for us at the price of His blood. But He entrusted the exercise of the power of absolution to the apostolic ministry which He charged with the 'ministry of reconciliation'" (CCC, No. 1442).

We see this clearly in John 20:19-23. On the evening that Jesus arose from the dead, He appeared to the apostles and said, "Peace be with you. As the Father has sent me, even so I send you." Scripture says that Jesus then breathed on the apostles and said, "Receive the Holy Spirit. If you forgive the sins of any, they are forgiven; if you retain the sins of any, they are retained." Here, Jesus endows the apostles with the Holy Spirit and then commissions them to be the human agents of His forgiveness. This ministry of reconciliation was meant not just for the apostles, but for all of their successors as well.

The early Christians understood the importance and benefit of receiving God's forgiveness through the ministry of a priest. For example in the *Didache*, a first century treatise on the teachings and practices of the early Church, we read: "Confess your offenses in Church, and do not go up to your prayer with an evil conscience." And later, "On the Day of the Lord gather together, break bread and give thanks after confessing your transgressions so that your sacrifice may be pure."

Around AD 80, St. Clement of Rome said to the Corinthian Church: "For it is good for a man to confess his failing rather than harden his heart." In his *Homilies on Leviticus* in AD 244, Origen praises the Christian "...who does not shrink from confessing his sins to a priest of the Lord." And in the fourth century, St. John Chrysostom taught, "Christ has given His priests a power He would not give to His angels, for has He not said to them, 'Whatsoever you bind on earth shall be bound in heaven'?"

In his book *Unabridged Christianity*, Father Mario Romero gives seven good reasons for receiving God's forgiveness through the ministry of a priest in the Sacrament of Penance:

1. We are seeking forgiveness the way Jesus designed it to be sought.
2. Through this sacrament, we receive graces that cleanse us from past wrongdoing *and* strengthen our spiritual resolve to avoid sin in the future.
3. We are *assured* of God's forgiveness through the audible words of the priest, Christ's representative on earth.
4. We can obtain sound advice on avoiding sin in the future by someone who is trained in the spiritual life.
5. We are reconciled with the larger faith community, whom our sin has adversely affected.
6. We make ourselves accountable for our actions, encouraging us to act more responsibly.
7. Mental health professionals tell us it is psychologically healthy to occasionally "unload" spiritual and emotional baggage in the presence of another human being who will listen non-judgmentally and relate to us with a compassionate heart.

Through the Sacrament of Penance, those who commit serious sin are reunited to the Body of Christ, so that grace-filled fellowship with God is restored. However, the Sacrament of Penance is not only for serious sin. It also helps us to overcome lesser sins and heals other weaknesses and frailties that are part of the human condition. The sweet balm of this healing sacrament restores, renews, and refreshes the wounded and troubled soul.

1. What are the five requirements for a good confession?

   a. ______________________________

   b. ______________________________

   c. ______________________________

   d. ______________________________

   e. ______________________________

2. Of the seven good reasons for receiving God's forgiveness in the Sacrament of Penance, which have I personally experienced? How did they help me in my life of faith?

   ____

   ____

   ____

WORD TO KNOW

Penance: Any prayer or good work imposed upon oneself or by a confessor. While the absolution of a priest takes away sin, it does not resolve the disorders that sin has caused. Sin weakens and injures the sinner, his relationship with God and his relationships with others. Raised up from sin, the sinner must still recover his spiritual health by making amends or "satisfaction" for his sin. This satisfaction is known as "penance."

FOR PONDERING...

Mended Hearts

In this chapter, Johnnette offers us a vivid description of her experience as a prodigal. As you read her story, note how contrition differs from regret. We may regret an action because it failed to accomplish what we intended, had unexpected negative consequences, or caused us to act contrary to our usual standards. Contrition, on the other hand, is the misery of realizing that we have offended God who loves us so much.

Some of us have been fervent Catholics from childhood. Most of us have at some time seriously departed from the right path. When we return, we experience Jesus in a new way, primarily as Mercy.

There was such a time in my own life. I was married, but very unhappy, and the mother of three live children (I had six miscarriages along the way). For the sake of the family I will not recount any details, but just say that my disordered attitudes took place in spite of my being a daily communicant who prayed more than an hour a day. I thought that these practices would make a serious sin impossible, but I was wrong.

When I went to my regular confessor, the priest interrupted my tearful story to get a book off the shelf. Then he slowly read me a short account of the life of a sinner who became a canonized saint. Receiving absolution, I felt Jesus draw me deeper into His heart than ever before; shortly after that, through consecration to the Immaculate Heart of Mary, I received graces of mystical prayer I had rarely experienced before my fall.

In the lessons to come many sins will be mentioned, some you might not even know are objective evils. Jesus never wants us to despair about big sins or chronic little ones. Saint Philip Neri, a sixteenth century saint, was told about a woman who was in despair, convinced she was going to hell even though she had repented of her sins. Philip went to visit her. He asked her: "Whom did Jesus save on the cross?"

"Sinners," she replied.

"Who are you?"

"A sinner."

"Therefore, as long as you repent, you are certainly not lost, but saved."

RC

Have I ever committed a sin I considered to be greater than God's mercy? How has this lesson helped me think differently?

____

____

____

IN CLOSING...

"Thou art the third light granted to the order of my beloved Francis. He was the first, among the Friars Minor; Clare was the second, among the nuns; thou shalt be the third, in the Order of Penance."

WORDS OF OUR LORD TO ST. MARGARET OF CORTONA

In place of a closing prayer today, make an examination of conscience. If possible, go to confession this week.

Chapter Four

Obedience: Power for the Abundant Life

Full of Grace: This week covers pages 79 to 103 of the text.

Our world is filled with images of power. Look around you this week, and notice how often politicians, advertisements, jobs, relationships, even song lyrics make some appeal to power. Power is intoxicating, and many have sold their souls for a slice of worldly power. We could laugh at their error, except that the resulting disorder, disharmony and chaos affect the whole world, and that's no laughing matter.

The cardboard power the world lusts after is not the same power that man lost in the Garden of Eden, when his disobedience severed him from his Creator—the Source of all power. Jesus was clear: "All power is given unto me in heaven and in earth" (Matthew 28:18). That power — lost to us in the Garden — is the empowering of the Holy Spirit, which comes to us through Christ Jesus.

The lessons that follow include keen insights into the relationship between obedience to God and power for victorious living. You will find practical applications of important principles to aid your quest for a more authentic feminine life with the power to transform the world around you.

LESSON ONE — Love: The Perfect Motivation For Obedience
LESSON TWO — What Does God Want From Us?
LESSON THREE — The Way to Triple Harmony with God: Poverty, Chastity and Obedience
LESSON FOUR — Balm for the Wounded Soul: The Practice of Detachment
LESSON FIVE — Obedience to the Prompting of the Holy Spirit

Questions To Ponder This Week

- What motivates me to do the good things that I do? What virtues do I have that help me to obey the Commandments, the precepts of the Church and God's special plan for my life?
- Am I aware of which of the world's allurements tug at me the most? What draws me away from perfection as a daughter of God, a Woman of Grace? What is the antidote to such tugs?

Media Response Sheet

Obedience: Power for the Abundant Life

Answer the following questions as you watch the pre-recorded lesson given by Johnnette S. Benkovic, founder of Women of Grace®.

WEEKLY THEME
Rejecting images of power and embracing obedience to the will of God restores order and victorious living.

WEEKLY GRACE
I pray for the grace to be docile to God's Commandments and faithful to His Church.

1. What will we be talking about in this lesson?

____

2. What does obedience always bring?

____

3. What is the quest of the spiritual life?

____

____

4. St. Bernard said, "Take away ______________________ and there will no longer be any ______________."

5. Why does God want us to obey Him?

____

6. What does God's signified will tell us?

____

7. In what three areas does God's signified will require obedience?

   a. ____

   b. ____

   c. ____

8. The Ten Commandments of God keep us out of ______________________________.

9. Ephesians 4:22 tells us that when we resist the commands of God, we are acting out of our ______________ __________, but when we follow the will of God by keeping His commandments and following the teaching of His Church, we begin to be ______________________ by the ______________________.

10. What is this "former way of life that deteriorates through illusion and desire"?

____

____

11. How does God offer us additional help and guidance?

____

____

12. In so many cases we have fallen victim to ____________________ rather than the __________________ of ________________________.

13. God does not ask for our ______________________. He asks for our ______________________.

14. What are the three evangelical counsels?

a. ____

b. ____

c. ____

15. What is the spiritual danger in not following the evangelical counsels?

____

____

16. In what other way are we to be obedient to God?

____

____

Woman of Grace

St. Therese of Lisieux (1873 – 1897)

Hidden behind the walls of the Carmelite convent she entered at age fifteen, St. Therese was struck down by tuberculosis in her early twenties. There was nothing remarkable about the young nun, nothing to suggest that she would become one of the most beloved of all the saints. And yet, her "little way," characterized by the twin virtues of obedience and simplicity, touched so many people that Rome opened her cause for canonization only seventeen years after her death. She was canonized in 1925, proclaimed the universal patron of missions in 1927, and Doctor of the Church by Pope John Paul II in 1997.

Marie Frances Therese Martin was born in Alencon, France to a devout Catholic couple with eight other children, only five of whom survived to adulthood. Therese's idyllic childhood was cut short at the tender age of four when her mother died. Big sister Pauline raised little Therese in the faith until 1882, when Pauline and another sister Marie entered the Discalced Carmelite convent in Lisieux. Their example made young Therese yearn for religious life herself. On a visit to Rome in November 1887, she and a group of pilgrims were granted an audience with Pope Leo XIII. At that audience, Therese asked permission from the Holy Father to enter the Carmelite convent at the age of fifteen.

When her postulancy was completed, Therese ventured outside her cloister one last time, where she received her habit. In her autobiography, *Story of a Soul,* she writes: "I had always wished that on the day I received the habit, nature would be adorned in white just like me." That January day, the weather was so mild, snow seemed unlikely. However, upon returning to the cloister, says Therese, "...the first thing that struck my eye was the statue of 'the little Jesus' smiling at me from the midst of flowers and lights. Immediately afterwards my glance was drawn to the snow: the monastery garden was white like me! What thoughtfulness on the part of Jesus! Anticipating the desires of his fiancée, He gave her snow. Snow! What mortal bridegroom, no matter how powerful he may be, could make snow fall from heaven to charm his beloved?"

The "Little Flower," as she came to be called, did not aspire to doing great works, or attaining public acclaim. Rather, she followed the way of perfection outlined by the founder of her order, St. Teresa of Avila. As Therese explained to her sisters: "Great deeds are forbidden me. I cannot preach the gospel nor shed my blood — but what does it matter? My brothers toil instead of me and I, a little child, keep close by the throne of God and I love for those who fight. Love proves itself by deeds. I will scatter flowers, perfuming the Divine Throne, and I'll sweetly sing my hymn of love. These flowers are every little sacrifice, every glance and word, and the doing of the least of actions for love."

She taught this simple way to the novices entrusted in her care, and so ministered to her missionary "brothers" whom she followed in her heart with love and prayers. From the first time she coughed up blood until her death three months later, she continued to draw ever more closely into the heart of her Beloved Spouse, seeking to become less and less, that she might fly like a bird to her heavenly home.

When her body was exhumed in 1910, the palm St. Therese held in her hand was still green, and from her final resting place came the sweet "odor of sanctity," the inexplicable aroma of violets. This humble sister had vowed, "My mission, to make God loved, will begin after my death. I will spend my heaven doing good on earth." And as she predicted, the miracles attributed to her circle the globe, causing her to be named the patroness of missions. Her little way that continues to inspire those who desire to love God, as she did, in simple obedience.

FAITH IN ACTION

How can I emulate the "little way" in my own life?

Woman of Grace

St. Gianna Beretta Molla, (Martyr of Maternal Love 1922 – 1962)

St. Gianna is called a "martyr of maternal love" for her heroic pro-life witness. In a letter to her future husband a few days before their marriage, she wrote: *"Love is the most beautiful sentiment the Lord has put into the soul of men and women."* She lived out these words in every aspect of her life. As a pediatrician, she devoted her leisure to teaching young men and women about Jesus and His Church. As a wife and mother, her enthusiasm for her vocation was obvious to all.

At the age of 39, while pregnant with her fourth child, Gianna was diagnosed with an ovarian cyst. Rejecting her doctors' advice to have an abortion, she underwent surgery to remove the painful cyst, which was endangering the baby in her womb. She said, "With faith and hope I have entrusted myself to the Lord... I renew to the Lord the offer of my life. I am ready for everything, to save my baby." As the time came for her delivery, Gianna instructed her husband Pietro, "If you must decide between me and the baby, have no hesitation. Choose—and I demand it—the baby, save him."

On Good Friday, April 20, 1962, Gianna delivered her child, Gianna Emmanuela. A week later, the young woman died from a painful infection, a contemporary witness of the importance of motherhood and the boundless love to which women are called. Her husband and children were among those present at Gianna's canonization on May 18, 2004 in Saint Peter's Square.

On the Feast of All Saints in 1999, a stained glass window of Blessed Gianna was installed in the chapel of the Newman Centre of Toronto. Gianna's daughter, Dr. Gianna Emanuela Molla, composed a prayer for the dedication ceremony (below). This week, reflect on her words, and consider how they encourage you to imitate St. Gianna's example of motherhood more fully in your own life.

> *Three days ago, when Padre Tom showed me the church windows for the first time and I saw my mother smiling, I was filled with joy and so pleased, because I have always imagined her in this way, knowing that the message of her life couldn't be represented better.*
>
> *Every moment of her entire existence was a real testimony of Christian love and faith, lived concretely and with joy in everyday life.... She is always with me, and since the momentous day of April 24, 1994, I have felt myself to be part of an ever-growing family comprised of so many people throughout the world who, like me, pray to her, confide in her, and feel close to her. I believe that this is also the design of Divine Providence, that now I shall never be alone.*

God, You who are Father, we give You praise and we bless You,
because in Gianna Beretta Molla You... have made known
a woman who witnessed [to the truth of] the Gospel
as a young person, as a bride, as a mother and a doctor.
Through the gift of ... [her] life,
we learn to accept and honor every human being....
Through her married love, she became a sign of Your love
for the Church and for humanity.

Holy Spirit, font of every perfection, give us wisdom, intelligence, and courage.
Grant that, like St. Gianna [my mother], and through her intercession,
we may put ourselves at the service of every person,
in our personal, family, and professional life....
and so to grow in love and in holiness. Amen.

Lesson One

Love: The Perfect Motivation For Obedience

Act of Consecration to the Sacred Heart of Jesus

O Sacred Heart of Jesus,
filled with infinite love,
broken by my ingratitude,
pierced by my sins, yet loving me still —
accept the consecration that I make to You
of all that I am and all that I have.
Take every faculty of my soul and body.
Draw me, day by day,
nearer and nearer to Your Sacred Heart,
and there, as I can bear the lesson,
teach me Your blessed ways. Amen.

WEEKLY THEME

Rejecting images of power and embracing obedience to the will of God restores order and victorious living.

WEEKLY GRACE

I pray for the grace to be docile to God's Commandments and faithful to His Church.

Full of Grace: Read pages 79 – 82 in the text, then answer the following questions.

1. Why is obedience necessary for the Christian life?

___

___

___

2. What are the three dispositions of heart with which we can obey? Can you give an example of each from your own life?

___

___

___

3. Who is the source of obedience?

___

___

___

___

4. What is God's ultimate will for us?

____

____

____

KNOW THE FAITH

The Voice of Conscience

Many people today say that certain behaviors or practices are a "matter of conscience." While this statement is true, it is inappropriate to use it to justify questionable actions. Sadly, this is all too often exactly what happens. In reality, a conscience must be properly formed before it can rightly discern between good and evil. Only then will the conscience fulfill the two purposes for which God designed it: to help us understand moral truth, that we might direct our life by its light; and to assist us in integrating every area of life with our commitment of faith.

Conscience is a reasoned judgment concerning the moral value of an act about to be or already performed or omitted; however, this "reasoned judgment" must be formed according to the laws of God. According to St. Paul, God has written His law on the heart of man (the natural law) and it both confronts us with the law of God and becomes a witness of our faithfulness to it (see Romans 2:13-15).

In *Our Sunday Visitor's Encyclopedia of Catholic Doctrine*, Patrick Lee gives five guidelines for forming the conscience properly:

1. Commit to growing in moral wisdom and to discerning, with God's grace, the moral truth about every aspect of our life.
2. Pray to the Father for the gift of enlightenment through the Holy Spirit in this regard (James 1:5-6).
3. Strive to appropriate the truth of the Gospel and integrate it into the intellect, emotions, and imagination. Only then are we able to evaluate what is morally good.
4. Ask the advice of sound counselors, to avoid falling into self-deception and rationalization.
5. Continue to study Church teaching, which should be the primary source by which the conscience is formed. It should be looked upon as a precious source of light, not a burden.

There are two kinds of poorly formed conscience. The first is "inculpably erroneous" or "invincibly ignorant." In this case, a person is not at fault for his actions, for he is ignorant of what is required by the moral law and, therefore, has no way to know the truth. However, as the five guidelines to forming a conscience tell us, we have a responsibility and a duty to take necessary and reasonable steps to learn the truth and to discover what is God's will for us in the decisions we face.

The second type of erroneously formed conscience is called "culpably erroneous conscience" or "vincible ignorance." This ignorance of the truth is the result of failing to find out what is required. This failure can be either willful (as in the case of a person who knows that he is in error but refuses to change) or the result of neglect (a failure to embrace truth out of laziness, disinterest, or an unwillingness to put truth above one's own desires).

Several factors can contribute to a culpably erroneous conscience: habitual sin, rationalization, individualistic notion of conscience, rejection of the Church's authority and her teaching, and lack of conversion and charity. The influence of our secularized culture and society is also a factor. Forming judgments and opinions according to worldly wisdom rather than the laws of God leads to an erroneous conscience. St. Paul admonishes us in Romans 12:2: "Do not be conformed to this world but be transformed by the renewal of your mind, that you may prove what is the will of God, what is good and acceptable and perfect."

Let us pray for the grace of renewal, that we might bring every area of life into conformity with the will of God as revealed to us through the Ten Commandments, Sacred Scripture, and the teachings of the Catholic Church.

1. Why does our conscience need to be informed?

____

____

____

2. What steps do I personally take to form my conscience according to the will of God? How can I do this better?

____

____

____

WORD TO KNOW

Secularism: A view of life that rejects the reality of God as well as the existence of permanent and objective good and evil.

FOR PONDERING...

The Measure of Our Love

Generally speaking, those of us whose parents were wise, gentle, and understanding authority figures have little trouble with obedience to God or the legitimate rules of Church and state. On the other hand, children whose parents or other authority figures were rigid, abusive, or lacking in empathy, tend to question or rebel against authority later in life. Most of us are somewhere in between. Meeting with intelligent, wise people in charge, we will readily obey. When we encounter rules that we think are stupid or excessive, we tend to question, evade, or rebel.

In the Old Testament, we read that the fear of the Lord is the beginning of wisdom. Terror of punishment and desire for reward play a large role in God's insistence on obedience in both the Old and the New Covenant. If you think Jesus only asked us to obey out of love and never out of fear or desire for reward, check His words carefully. There are plenty of warnings about punishment and reward. Even though there is much in the Old Testament about God's merciful love (and even more in the New Testament), Jesus emphasizes love of the Father as the main reason for obedience. In love, Jesus himself obeyed the Father.

On the farm, a horse must sometimes be coaxed with a carrot, other times with a stick or whip. We see this in secular law as well. For example, how often would you strictly follow speeding laws, especially on deserted roads, if there were no police?

God also uses different methods in His dealings with us. At times we need to be reminded of the consequences of our actions, and of the punishments in store for those who disobey God's commands. On the other hand, doing something out of obedience— simply to please another person—produces a kind of joy that fear of punishment and craving of distant rewards rarely bring.

For example, think of the obligation to participate in Sunday Mass. Some days, even daily communicants just don't feel like going to Church. We can go just because it is a law of the Church, to avoid committing a mortal sin by missing Sunday Mass without a serious reason; we can also go because we want God to reward us on the Day of Judgment for strict compliance with His will.

How much better, though, if we think: "How disappointed Jesus will be if on His special day, a Sunday holiday that wouldn't even exist without His influence on Christian society, He doesn't see me, His beloved daughter, coming to receive Him?"

RC

How can I help myself to obey out of love rather than fear?

____

____

____

____

IN CLOSING...

"Christ does not force our will, He only takes what we give Him. But He does not give Himself entirely until He sees that we yield ourselves entirely to Him."

ST. TERESA OF AVILA

Thank You, Lord, for loving me enough not to leave me as I am; instead You urge me onward and upward, and give me strength to follow You always. Stay beside me, precious Lord. Amen.

Lesson Two

What Does God Want from Us?

Prayer of St. Therese of Lisieux

O my God! I ask you for myself and those dear to me
the grace to fulfill perfectly your holy will
And to accept for love of you the joys and sorrows
of this passing life so that one day
We may be reunited in Heaven for all eternity. Amen

WEEKLY THEME

Rejecting images of power and embracing obedience to the will of God restores order and victorious living.

WEEKLY GRACE

I pray for the grace to be docile to God's Commandments and faithful to His Church.

Full of Grace: Read pages 82 to 87, then answer the following questions.

1. In your own words, define the signified will of God. Describe how the story of the rich young man displays the signified will of God.

2. What three sources of guidance does God give us to help us "adjust perspective?"

3. Do I need a perspective adjustment in any of the areas mentioned on page 86? What causes me to resist?

4. Describe a time when you were obedient to a Gospel command or teaching of the Church even when it was difficult.

KNOW THE FAITH
On Human Life

In 1968, Pope Paul VI wrote an encyclical called *Humanae Vitae* ("On Human Life"), which upheld the clear and consistent teaching of the Catholic Church that contraception is intrinsically wrong. This letter sent shock waves not only through the Catholic community but through the entire Western world as well. Many thought the Church would change her position on contraception because of a perceived population explosion, the advancement of women into the workforce and professions, and the development of the birth control pill. The letter, released at the height of the sexual revolution, was met with hostility, anger, and dissent.

Though the backlash continues to this present day, the Church holds fast to her teaching that contraception is a great moral wrong because it violates God's intention and purpose for the sexual act. The two "goods" of conjugal union are its procreative dimension and its unitive dimension. In other words, sex is, by its very nature, ordered to the begetting of children and the bonding of the husband and wife in total self-giving love. To use contraception in the sexual act is to deny both of its goods: children cannot be conceived and the husband and wife withhold from each other a fundamental aspect of themselves—their fertility.

The Holy Father did recognize, however, that serious physical, psychological, and external conditions may exist within a family, which may cause a couple for prudential reasons to space or otherwise limit the birth of children. In these situations, the Holy Father urges couples to regulate births by cooperating with the rhythms of nature and refraining from sexual union during the woman's fertile cycle. In so doing, "the married couple make legitimate use of a natural disposition" rather than "impeding the development of the natural processes," as is the case with contraception.

In paragraph seventeen of the encyclical, Pope Paul VI clearly states what he saw as the grave consequences of using artificial birth control. The paragraph states in part:

> *"[C]onsider, first of all, how wide and easy a road would thus be opened up towards conjugal infidelity and the general lowering of morality. Not much experience is needed in order to know human weakness, and to understand that men — especially the young, who are so vulnerable on this point — have need of encouragement to be faithful to the moral law, so that they must not be offered some easy means of eluding its observance. It is also to be feared that the man, growing used to the employment of anti-conceptive practices, may finally lose respect for the woman and, no longer caring for her physical and psychological equilibrium, may come to the point of considering her as a mere instrument of selfish enjoyment, and no longer as his respected and beloved companion.*
>
> *"Let it be considered that a dangerous weapon would thus be placed in the hands of those public authorities who take no heed of moral exigencies… Who will stop rulers from favoring, from even imposing upon their peoples if they were to consider it necessary, the method of contraception which they judge to be most efficacious?*
>
> *"Consequently, if the mission of generating life is not to be exposed to the arbitrary will of men, one must necessarily recognize insurmountable limits to the possibility of man's domination over his own body and its functions …And such limits cannot be determined otherwise than by the respect due to the integrity of the human organism and its functions…."*

Pope Paul VI, knowing that the voice of dissent would arise on this issue, underscored that the mission of the Church was to be, as that of her divine founder, a "sign of contradiction," proclaiming with humble firmness the entire moral law, both natural and evangelical. With pastoral concern, he exhorted all people to accept this teaching with docility, integrity, and fortitude.

1. How does contraception violate the two "goods" of the sexual union?

2. In what ways have Pope Paul VI's concerns about the consequences of artificial birth control come to pass?

WORD TO KNOW

Dissent: Refusal to conform to the authority of an established civil or religious institution. The Catholic who dissents refuses to accept something taught authoritatively or dogmatically by the Church's solemn or ordinary Magisterium, substitutes one's own judgment for that of the Church, and demonstrates a lack of understanding of Christ's presence in the Church. To dissent is to risk losing one's Catholic identity and to render oneself ineffective for the work of evangelization (*Our Sunday Visitor's Encyclopedia of Catholic Doctrine*, by Cormac Burke).

FOR PONDERING...

Subject to... No One?

For the most of my adult life, I was subject to no one. Even when I became a Christian, I would willingly submit to the elders of my Evangelical Church only so long as I thought they were correct. But to be Protestant is to be free to disagree with those in authority of a particular faith community or, if pressed, free to find one that subscribes to (or at least tolerates) a particular theological or ecclesiological perspective. If no such church exists, a dissenting Protestant may well start his own "home church."

I became Catholic because I came to believe that the Catholic Church is indeed the Church that Christ, the Jewish Messiah, God in human flesh, established on earth. I came to believe that the Church is not man's institution, but God's — the Church Christ established and promised to lead into all truth until the end of time.

One day on Mother Angelica Live, a woman asked me: "Didn't you have a problem with that big book (the Catechism) when you came into the Church? All those rules and regulations? You seem like a fairly independent, intelligent woman. Didn't you have trouble submitting to all that?"

I told her that the Catechism is to me what a playpen is to a two-year-old. Why do you put a toddler in a playpen? To protect him—and your house as well! And so God, who formed us for Himself, has put a "playpen" around us—the Commandments and the infallible teachings of His Church—to protect us and to protect others.

"But who are you, Catholic Church, to tell us what to do?" Some, even within the Church, ask that question. "Who are you to tell us what to do with our bodies? Who are you to think you're the only act in town? Don't you realize that the Church's teachings on contraception, sterilization, abortion, same-sex unions and other issues are archaic? Why don't you get with the program? You have no right to tell us what to do and what to believe. You have a right to your ideas; but you have no right to impose them on us!"

I say to such unbelieving souls: "They are not our ideas, they are God's ideas. The Church has no right to invent truth, nor can it. But it has been given the mandate to deliver God's truth, to teach the faith once delivered to the saints and handed down in an unbroken line of apostolic succession for 2,000 years."

I have learned in my own life the truth of our Lord's words. Jesus said, "You shall know the truth and the truth will make you free." Free from what? From death, destruction, despair, sin, Satan, and hell. Free to what? Free to follow God, to be all He created you to be, to be happy, and fruitful, to have a life more wonderful than you could ever have imagined.

If you've wandered from the fold, the Master is calling you. Will He change His Commandments and the eternal truth He has entrusted to His Church? No. But, if you come to Him with a contrite heart, a heart of obedience to His love, He will give you life and meaning and purpose and love and fulfillment beyond all you've ever imagined. You shall know the truth, and the truth will set you free — free to be all you were meant to be. God bless you.

RM

John 8:32 says, "...you will know the truth, and the truth will make you free." What do you think is the relationship between truth and freedom, and between lack of truth and bondage?

IN CLOSING...

On leaving home to enter the convent, St. Margaret Mary Alacoque declared, "I felt like a slave freed from prison and chains to enter the house of her beloved... to rejoice, absolutely free, in his presence, his riches, his love."

Father God, search my heart. Let me see clearly those areas of my life that, out of pride or self-will, I have withheld from embracing the truth You entrusted to the Church. Change my heart, and help me to accept even those things I do not fully understand, with joyful assent. Amen.

Lesson Three

The Way to Triple Harmony With God: Poverty, Chastity, and Obedience

WEEKLY THEME

Rejecting images of power and embracing obedience to the will of God restores order and victorious living.

WEEKLY GRACE

I pray for the grace to be docile to God's Commandments and faithful to His Church.

Prayer: Litany of Humility

O Jesus! Meek and humble of Heart, hear me.
From the desire of being esteemed,
Deliver me, Jesus.
From the desire of being loved… (Deliver…)
From the desire of being extolled…
From the desire of being honored…
From the desire of being praised…
From the desire of being preferred to others…
From the desire of being consulted…
From the desire of being approved…
From the fear of being humiliated…
From the fear of being despised…
From the fear of suffering rebukes…
From the fear of being calumniated…
From the fear of being forgotten…
From the fear of being ridiculed…
From the fear of being wronged…
From the fear of being suspected…

That others may be loved more than I,
Jesus, grant me the grace to desire it.
That others may be esteemed more than I… (Jesus…)
That, in the opinion of the world, others may
increase and I may decrease…
That others may be chosen and I set aside…
That others may be praised and I unnoticed…
That others may be preferred to me in everything…
That others may become holier than I, provided that I may become as holy as I should…

MERRY CARDINAL DEL VAL

***Full of Grace:* Read pages 87 - 92 in the text, and then answer the following questions.**

1. In your own words, describe the "triple harmony."

2. What are the three moral wounds and what caused them?

3. To what do the three moral wounds attach us?

4. What is an attachment with which I struggle and why?

KNOW THE FAITH

The Tell-Tale Signs of Pride

Let's take a little test. There is only one requirement — that we be honest with ourselves.

DO I...		
Evaluate all things by the affect it will have on my family or me?	YES ( )	NO ( )
Boast about accomplishments — overtly or subtly?	YES ( )	NO ( )
Put my own preferences above that of others?	YES ( )	NO ( )
Feel the need to command (or control) every situation?	YES ( )	NO ( )
Talk about myself and my own concerns in every conversation?	YES ( )	NO ( )
Want people to have a good opinion of me, at any price?	YES ( )	NO ( )
Use every opportunity to point out another's mistakes?	YES ( )	NO ( )
"Bad mouth" others?	YES ( )	NO ( )
Get impatient when contradicted or corrected?	YES ( )	NO ( )
Want to be "in the know?"	YES ( )	NO ( )
Enjoy the limelight?	YES ( )	NO ( )
Refuse to readily admit faults, if at all?	YES ( )	NO ( )
Try to cover up or excuse sins — even in confession?	YES ( )	NO ( )
Believe deep down inside that I am better than others in any way, be it socially, spiritually, or morally?	YES ( )	NO ( )
Attribute any and all success to my own efforts?	YES ( )	NO ( )
Cling to self-complacency?	YES ( )	NO ( )
Get irritated (even slightly) if someone else gets attention and praise?	YES ( )	NO ( )

SCORE NO _______ YES _______

If we are honest with ourselves, we most likely have checked "yes" to a number of the above boxes. Pride, that first of all sins, has placed us at the center of our own universe, and encouraged us to determine for ourselves what is right and wrong, what our own moral standard should be, how justice should be meted out.

As a people and as a culture, we desperately need to recover the virtue of humility, the "queen-mother" of all the virtues. Humility restores our perspective. It roots out self-centeredness and presumption, dismisses haughtiness and arrogance, and harnesses unbridled ambition. Unlike pride, humility begins with truth — the truth about who we are and who God is. The truth about the real motives behind our actions, words, and deeds. The truth about our fallen condition. The truth about our sinfulness. The truth about our need for God. The truth about our dependence upon Him for all things. As St. Teresa of Avila simply states, humility is "walking in the truth."

Many counterfeits masquerade as humility. The first is the pretense of humility. St. Francis de Sales says, "True humility makes no pretense of being humble, and scarcely ever utters a word of humility." False humility, on the other hand, is often found behind words of self-abnegation and unworthiness. In many cases, the words simply camouflage a soul brimming over with pride and self-sufficiency.

True humility does not denigrate or deny outright the gifts and talents we have been given. Archbishop Fulton Sheen once said, "A man who is six feet tall but who says, 'I am only five feet tall,' is not humble. He who is a good writer is not humble if he says: 'I am a scribbler.' Such statements are made in order that there might be a denial and thus win praise. Rather he would be humbler who says: 'Well, whatever talent I have is a gift of God and I thank Him for it.'"

Remember — humility is truth. Each of us has gifts and talents; to acknowledge the God who gave them to us admits that He is the First Cause of who we are, what we do, and all we accomplish.

Still another counterfeit of true humility is feigned disregard for compliments or praise. St. Bernard says, "It is no great thing to be humble when you are brought low; but to be humble when you are praised is a great and rare attainment." False humility reacts in one of two ways to compliments and praise. The first is an ego-need to be assured of a job well done. The second is to be overly reserved about accepting compliments and praise. In both cases, the false humility is rooted in the assumption that somehow we are responsible for what we have done, rather than the God who accomplishes all in all. The humble soul is happy to be an instrument through which the love and mercy of God can shine, without in any way assigning the luster to self.

Pride sometimes masquerades as a fear to attempt great things. How many great works for the kingdom of God have been thwarted because of this counterfeit! When God desires we tackle a certain task, typically the fear of saying "yes" to these inspirations of grace falls into one of three main categories: the fear of failure, the fear of losing creature comforts, and the fear of losing social standing. We must be willing to risk all these things for the kingdom of God once we are assured of His will in a particular matter.

The last counterfeit of true humility is complacency toward the spiritual life. The sure sign of someone growing in holiness is the person who feels that he is but a beginner in the spiritual life, no matter what level of union with God he has attained. It is pride that causes us to believe we are holier than we are, that we have attained exemplary spiritual merits, that we have acquired the height of mystical union. This false notion about ourselves allows complacency to root in our hearts, and does much to undermine our relationship with God. Soon, a lukewarm attitude toward prayer and to God Himself overcomes our zeal, and the capital sin of *acedia* (spiritual sloth) sets in.

Pride always produces deadly fruit: presumption, ambition, and vainglory. Humility, on the other hand, brings peace, fervor and spiritual productivity. To safeguard against pride and to engender the virtue of humility, we must contemplate the majesty of God (see James 4:6; Matthew 6:2; John 15:5; 1 Corinthians 4:7; 2 Corinthians 3:5; Philippians 2:3). As we contemplate the person of Jesus Christ; develop an active prayer life; and accept the contradictions of daily life as "treasures of humility," we may hope to grow in this queen of all virtues.

1. How is pride most likely to show itself in my life?

____

____

____

2. Which "counterfeit humility" do I see manifesting itself?

____

____

____

3. Which of the four safeguards can I employ to overcome?

____

____

____

WORD TO KNOW

Concupiscence: A general attraction or inclination toward evil, particularly toward bodily and fleshly pleasures. Concupiscence arises in the imagination and arouses the sensual appetites. Concupiscence and passion are not sinful in themselves; they are forces that lead to sin: "Rather, each person is tempted when he is lured and enticed by his own desire. Then desire conceives and brings forth sin, and when sin reaches maturity it gives birth to death" (James 1: 14-15, NAB).

FOR PONDERING

The Holy Exchange

In a series of lectures on women's issues, which Saint Teresa Benedicta of the Cross (Edith Stein) gave between the two World Wars, this outstanding woman philosopher described certain virtues common to most women and also certain negative traits more often found in women than in men. They are:

POSITIVE FEMININE TRAITS:	NEGATIVE FEMININE TRAITS:
affectionate, attentive, caring, careful, charming, compassionate, considerate, delicate, diplomatic, empathetic, gentle, giving, gracious, hospitable, intimate, intuitive, long-suffering, neat, nurturing, polite, pure, sensitive, sharing, soft, submissive, sweet, understanding, warm, wise.	catty, chattering, clinging, comfort loving, complaining, curious (in the sense of invading another's privacy or needing to be "in the know") overly-dependent, overly-emotional, envious, jumpy, manipulative, mean, meddling, moody, nagging, petty, pious, prudish, seductive, overly-sentimental, silly, shopping-addicted, smothering, touchy, vain, weak, worried.

Each of us has traits from both lists. We jealously guard "our" indulgences, faults, and peccadilloes. Too often we see those traits as part of our identity. Yet only the positive traits produce lasting fruit in our lives. Women of Grace® study sessions help us to unravel the negative from the positive in our lives. The history of each saint is in reality the story of how she sought harmony with God through the events and trials of her life, how she surrendered her negatives in exchange for holy traits that made her more like her Father! ("Be ye perfect, even as your Father in heaven is perfect.")

Harmonious living might be expressed as an equation — harmony increases in proportion to the strength of the virtues of poverty, chastity, and obedience. Each of these evangelical counsels contains some of the traits in the positive feminine list. The key to achieving harmony with God rests on our willingness to surrender our negative traits, conforming our minds and will to God.

RC

Go through the list of Positive Feminine Traits. Highlight the ones you have and circle the one you most need to develop. Think up one strategy that you can use this week to help acquire that positive trait. Now, go through the list of Negative Feminine Traits. Highlight the ones you have. Which one trait do you think the Holy Spirit is giving you the grace to overcome? (Hint: Which one do you confess most frequently?) What one strategy can you use this week to overcome this one trait?

IN CLOSING...

"The Blessed Virgin chose me because I was the most ignorant. If she had found any one more ignorant than myself, she would have chosen her. The Blessed Virgin used me like a broom. What do you do with a broom when you have finished sweeping? You put it back in its place, behind the door."

ST. BERNADETTE SOUBIROUS

It was no accident or cosmological happenstance that I was created as a woman. You deliberately chose every aspect of my being — my gender, my gifts, my talents — through which Your strength can shine most brightly. Lord, You would never ask me to do something without giving me the grace I need to do it. I place myself entirely in Your hands, to do with as You see fit. Amen.

Lesson Four

Balm for the Wounded Soul: The Practice of Detachment

Prayer to My Guardian Angel
Angel of God, my guardian dear
To whom God's love commits me here.
Ever this day be at my side
To light and guard,
To rule and guide. Amen.

WEEKLY THEME
Rejecting images of power and embracing obedience to the will of God restores order and victorious living.

WEEKLY GRACE
I pray for the grace to be docile to God's Commandments and faithful to His Church.

Full of Grace: Read pages 92 – 94 in the text, and then answer the following questions.

1. What are the spiritual antidotes to moral wounds?

2. Given my state in life, how am I called to live with a spirit of detachment?

3. How is this spirit of detachment cultivated?

4. In the section entitled "How to cultivate a spirit of detachment," which of the categories applies to me the most and why?

KNOW THE FAITH

Consumerism and the Human Person

As a philosopher, Pope John Paul II is a Christian "personalist." He sees each individual human being as a unique and unrepeatable person made in the image and likeness of God, whose primary vocation is to give himself to God and to others in love. The human person reflects God's image and likeness in three distinct ways:

- in rationality,
- in self-consciousness, and
- in free will.

Each of these three things help a person to achieve his vocation to love. Because every person is made in the image and likeness of God, each individual — regardless of social class, nationality, or state or stage of life — has inestimable dignity and worth. Therefore, the human person takes primacy over the rest of God's creation as well as over any and all social systems (ie, political, economic, or legal), which are to serve the human person, protect his dignity and worth, and help him achieve his ultimate vocation. Any system that devalues the human person and/or thwarts his ability or freedom to realize his vocation is evil.

It is from this understanding of the human person that Pope John Paul II voices strong condemnations regarding our consumer-oriented contemporary culture. The consumerist society bases a person's worth on what he has or what he can produce, rather than who he is. Thus, a person is tempted to live according to "having" rather than "being," and the acquisition of goods becomes his goal, his way of life, and the source of his identity. This dehumanizes the person, for it causes him to lose sight of his true identity (a person made in the image and likeness of God) and true vocation (to give himself to God and to others in love). Instead he becomes a "consumer," one who consumes goods (or in some cases, even becomes the "goods"), rather than a "subject" who uses goods as a means to achieve his call to love.

At its worst, consumerism enslaves the human person. His freedom is lost as both his desire to possess and his possessions enslave him. In such a situation, the person's freedom to lovingly give of himself to God and to others is seriously impaired if not altogether destroyed. The chains of "having" enslave him and prevent him from attaining true happiness, peace and contentment; these attributes come only with self-giving love.

In his encyclical *Sollicitudo Rei Socialis* ("On Social Concerns"), Pope John Paul II speaks to this issue:

> *"... side-by-side with the miseries of underdevelopment, themselves unacceptable, we find ourselves up against a form of super-development, equally inadmissible, because like the former it is contrary to what is good and to true happiness. This super-development, which consists in an excessive availability of every kind of material goods for the benefit of certain social groups, easily makes people slaves of 'possession' and immediate gratification, with no other horizon than the multiplication or continual replacement of the things already owned with others still better. This is the so-called civilization of 'consumption' or 'consumerism,' which involves so much throwing-away and waste. An object already owned but now superseded by something better is discarded, with no thought of its possible lasting value... nor of some other human being who is poorer.*
>
> *"All of us experience firsthand the sad effects of this blind submission to pure consumerism: in the first place a crass materialism, and at the same time a radical dissatisfaction, because one quickly learns — unless one is shielded from the flood of publicity and the ceaseless and tempting offers of products — that the more one possesses the more one wants, while deeper aspirations remain unsatisfied and perhaps even stifled..."* (No. 28).

"When individuals and communities do not see a rigorous respect for the moral, cultural and spiritual requirements, based on the dignity of the person and on the proper identity of each community, beginning with the family and religious societies, then all the rest — availability of goods, abundance of technical resources applied to daily life, a certain level of material well-being — will prove unsatisfying and in the end contemptible. The Lord clearly says this in the Gospel, when he calls the attention of all to the true hierarchy of values: "For what will it profit a man, if he gains the whole world and forfeits his life?" (Matthew 16:26) (No. 33)

1. What are some of the ways you have seen the consumerist mentality "take over" a person's life? To what extent has it affected you?

 ____

 ____

2. How can a person use goods so as to give himself in love?

 ____

 ____

WORD TO KNOW

Hierarchy: A series of ordered groupings of people or things within a system. A "hierarchy of values" refers to a scale of objective values ranked by their importance in light of the dignity and worth of the human person. From most important to least important they are: 1) religious values, 2) moral values, 3) human biological values.

FOR PONDERING…

Addicted to Stuff

I am a recovering "Stuff-oholic." I have struggled all my life with my own addiction to stuff. I come from a family of Yankee hoarders — people who couldn't throw anything away. My Uncle Hazen is a prime example of our family problem. He lived to be 83, and died because his paper bag collection caught on fire and putting it out put a strain on his heart. Possessions can kill you!

My family and I aren't the only ones who suffer with this problem. Many people, including those who believe they are faithful followers of Christ, don't understand the difference between prudence and hoarding, or are simply overwhelmed by the flood of objects that flow into their homes.

Some, on the other hand, pride themselves on their ability to save. Christians who are proud of their "thriftiness" may be horrified to realize that the scriptural words for their attitude are lust and greed. The Greek word for lust is *epithumeo;* St. Paul uses it in numbers of places. In Ephesians 2:3, he refers to "lusts of the flesh and lusts of the mind"; in Titus 2:12 he speaks of "worldly lusts"; and in Titus 4:3 and 2 Timothy 3:6 he speaks of "various lusts." St. John also warns his readers against loving the world by coveting or lusting in his first letter (1 John 2:15-17).

The Greek word for greed is *pleonexia*. Take a look at Mark 7:22 and Luke 12:13-21 to see what Jesus has to say about this vice, and Matthew 6:19-21 to see what he says about storing up earthly treasures. Christian women who complain that their problem is the need for more storage space must ask themselves if they are like the man in St. Luke's passage who thought he needed bigger barns. What these women probably need is less stuff.

Many good Christian women have attics, closets, basements, and garages full of "treasures" they most likely will never use. If they gave their excess to the poor before moths and rust destroyed it, they would be storing treasure in heaven. As it is, they are storing up condemnation.

Many Christian women sincerely desire to bear good fruit, but their lust for things chokes their good intentions. If hoarding has become a habit or a family tradition, then it will take time to replace it with the virtue of generosity. But today is the best day to start. How do you get started?

First, do the spiritual work necessary to do the physical work. Make a serious examination of conscience about this area of your life and go to the Sacrament of Confession as often and as frequently as necessary. God doesn't magically take away the fault or remove the temptation. He expects us to cooperate with His grace.

Don't make excuses for yourself or rationalize your behavior. Strive, instead, to change your attitude and your way of thinking about the things you own. Ask a family member, friend, or spiritual director to hold you accountable to this change in your life and don't get angry when they do.

Taking one room at a time, sort through your stuff to see what can be thrown away, given away, or — in a small quantity — stored away. The latter is usually a few mementos to remind you of significant events in your life or your family's life. Return borrowed items to their owners. Sell items of value that you no longer need (you may want to donate the proceeds to the poor).

Finally, take courage! Fight off discouragement, fear, and temptation! Keep moving forward and trust in God! It may take time, but with God's grace and the help He provides, you can make real progress in overcoming your addiction to stuff. Engaging the process is half the battle.

DO'L

To what extent am I "addicted to stuff?" To answer, consider the following: Do you have any of these "treasures" stored away?

- Bags of baby clothes, though your youngest is 25?
- Drawers of unmatched socks kept in the hopes that the mates will one day show up?
- Toys or games with missing pieces — maybe they will come in handy?
- Duplicates of household items — spares, just in case?
- Appliances that are broken, outdated, or haven't been used in the past ten years?
- Outdated books, almanacs, encyclopedias?
- Old newspapers, clippings, magazines?

How can I use what I have learned today to overcome this problem?

IN CLOSING...

"Do not be so anxious about a house on earth when we have such a beautiful one in heaven. We are poor, but charity compels us. We must share what God gives among the poor."

ST. SOLEDAD

Lord, You have entrusted so much to me. Make me more sensitive to the needs of those around me, and more generous with my time and treasure. Give me at least one opportunity this week to bless someone who has a need, in Your name. Amen.

Lesson Five

Obedience to the Promptings of the Holy Spirit

Prayer of John Paul II to Our Lady of Guadalupe

Dear Blessed Virgin of Guadalupe,
We beg you to grant us a great love of all the holy sacraments,
which are, as it were, the signs that your Son left us on earth.
Thus, Most Holy Mother,
with the peace of God in our consciences,
with our hearts free from evil and hatred,
we will be able to bring to all others true joy and true peace,
which come to us from your Son,
our Lord Jesus Christ,
who with the Father and the Holy Spirit,
lives and reigns for ever and ever.
Amen.

WEEKLY THEME

Rejecting images of power and embracing obedience to the will of God restores order and victorious living.

WEEKLY GRACE

I pray for the grace to be docile to God's Commandments and faithful to His Church.

Full of Grace: Read pages 94 – 103 in the text, and then answer the following questions.

1. Generally, how can we know if a "prompting" comes from the Holy Spirit?

2. What criteria help us evaluate if an extraordinary prompting is from God?

3. Which of the above criteria have I used and when? Describe the result.

4. In this section, Johnnette shares an experience from her life about a time when she obeyed a prompting of the Holy Spirit that yielded good fruit. What prompting have I obeyed that has yielded fruit in my life or in the life of someone else?

KNOW THE FAITH
The Precepts of the Church

Jesus tells us, "I have come that they might have life and have it more abundantly" (John 10:10). This abundant life is possible by the grace a soul experiences when it is obedient to the commandments of God.

Many Scripture passages speak to us about the relationship between life and obedience. Consider these examples:

- "My son, keep my commandments, and you will live" (Proverbs 7:1-2).
- "The steadfast love of the Lord is upon those who remember to do his commandments" (Psalms 103:7-18).
- "If you would enter life, keep the commandments" (Matthew 9:17).

As these passages point out, following the laws of God always leads us to the abundant life. Holy Mother Church, who has guardianship of the Commandments of God, also provides us with guidance and direction on attaining the abundant life Jesus promises. One way she does this is through the Precepts (or Commandments) of the Church. These precepts instill in the faithful a sense of responsibility and duty toward the Church and remind them of the absolute minimum necessary to keep their Christian faith alive.

Of course, a woman of grace who truly wants to grow in love of God and deeply desires to experience the fullness of life that Jesus promises will not be content with the "minimum" requirement. Rather, she will seek to make both the Commandments of God and the Commandments of His Church foundation stones upon which she builds her life.

The Precepts of the Church, as outlined in Catechism (2041–2043), include:

- Keep the Sundays and holy days of obligation by assisting at Mass and desisting from servile work.
- Go to confession at least once a year.
- Receive the Blessed Sacrament during the season of Easter.
- Fast and abstain on the days appointed by the Church.
- Contribute to the support of the church and its pastors.

As well as these five precepts, the bishops of the United States further stress that all Catholic Christians are to "join in the missionary spirit and apostolate of the Church."

1. Review the five precepts of the Church and make an examination of conscience according to them. For which ones do I exceed the minimum requirement? For which ones do I need to make a more concerted effort?

2. How do I personally and specifically "join in the missionary spirit and apostolate of the Church?" Is my effort in this area minimal and if so what one simple action can I take to become more involved?

WORD TO KNOW

Obedience: From the Latin meaning "to hear." In the biblical understanding, obedience has to do with entering into God's life itself and giving assent to his plan of revelation. To obey is to "hear" the will of God and respond to it wholeheartedly.

FOR PONDERING
Follow His Lead

We are supposed to do God's will. It would be most unloving of God to command us to do His will, and then refuse to tell us what His will for us is. Since God is loving, then it stands to reason that He does reveal His will to us.

We have the law of God and the teachings of the Church. If we have a question about right and wrong, we can look up the answer. It is never God's will for us to break His laws. When we are tempted to steal or cheat, we don't need to pray "Dear God should I commit this sin or not?" The answer is obvious: "Absolutely not."

But many of our decisions aren't choices between right and wrong, but choices between two good things. Some are big choices like whom to marry, where to go to school, and what job to take. Others are small decisions like whether or not to buy a particular pair of shoes. All our decisions are important and we should in the small things as well as the big, put every decision to prayer.

"Dear God, here I stand in the supermarket. You know what I need and you know how much money I have. Guide my eyes and my hands."

It may sound silly, but if you learn to trust God every day in the supermarket, when the big decisions come along you will find it much easier to hear His voice.

We can't know the future. We can't know all the circumstances that will affect the outcome of our decisions, but God does. If we pray, "God let me know your will and do it," He will guide us.

Several years ago my husband was about to enter into a very important business relationship. As he went out the door, he said, "Pray that if this isn't God's will, it won't go through." I prayed and the whole thing fell through. We were disappointed, but trusted that God had protected us. Sure enough, a few months later the person involved was arrested and charged with a felony.

We can never go wrong by heeding God's commandments, the teachings of His Church, and following His guidance and direction in the everyday and not-so-everyday decisions of our life.

DO'L

Has there been a time when obeying the commandments of God and/or the teachings of the Church safeguarded me from a trial or a dangerous outcome? When did heeding the prompting of God do the same for me or for someone I know?

____

____

____

____

IN CLOSING...

"Let nothing disturb thee, nothing frighten thee;
all things pass away, but God never changes.
Patience obtains all things.
She whom God possesses wants for nothing,
God alone suffices."

ST. TERESA OF AVILA

Yes, Lord. In 2 Corinthians 12: 9 You tell us that Your grace is sufficient for us and that our weaknesses are made strong in You. Help me to remember each day that You are all I need. Amen.

Chapter Five

Wisdom: Vision for the Abundant Life

Full of Grace: This week covers pages 105 – 137 of the text.

Wisdom eludes the profane but settles gently on the saints. God freely favors those who seek to understand all things with the mind of Christ. The rhythm of life rushes on, both joy and sorrow ride its crest. The human heart yearns for order and meaning—teach us, O Lord! Growing in wisdom is a process that each woman may embrace. The deepest contentment of life unfolds in the heart of the woman who surrenders her soul to God; and He, Lover of souls, rewards that ardor.

The lessons in this chapter will guide Women of Grace through a step-by-step spiritual renewal: preparation, growth in virtue and reflection on a life lived in God's providence. Within these pages you'll find both effective tools for the practice of spiritual excellence and inspiration from centuries of saintly women whose struggle to know God began as yours did: "Why did God make me?"

LESSON ONE — Wisdom Day by Day
LESSON TWO — Seed of Renewal: Renewing the Mind According to God's Standard
LESSON THREE — Seed of Virtue: Acting Upon God's Grace
LESSON FOUR — Seed of Holy Reflection: Seeing the Hand of God in Daily Life
LESSON FIVE — Spiritual Direction: Nurturing the Divine Life Within Us

Questions To Ponder This Week

- Am I aware of God's hand in my daily life? How can I learn to recognize His love for me in the midst of a frantic day, an illness, a celebration? How can I develop the eyes of faith?
- What do you want from me, dear God? Where are you leading me, Lord? As I continue past the halfway mark of this study, for what are you preparing me?

Media Response Sheet

Wisdom: Vision for the Abundant Life

Answer the following questions as you watch the pre-recorded lesson given by Johnnette S. Benkovic, founder of Women of Grace®.

WEEKLY THEME

Holy wisdom, the ability to see God working in and through all of life's circumstances, transforms our perspective and reveals the eternal value of all things.

WEEKLY GRACE

I pray for the grace of holy wisdom so that I may conform my life to the will of God's good pleasure.

1. As we grow in holiness, our reason for obedience changes from ______________________ to one of ____ ______________________, a desire ______________________.

2. What is God's will of good pleasure sometimes called?

____

____

____

3. Submitting to God's will of good pleasure calls forth from us all we have learned of ______________, all that we have learned of ______________, and all that we have learned of ______________. Thus, this submission brings us to ______________.

4. How do we conform ourselves to the will of God when it hurts very much?

____

____

____

____

5. What are the three grace-filled seeds that help us grow in wisdom?

____

____

6. How do we cultivate the seed of renewal?

a. __________

b. __________

c. __________

7. What is virtue?

8. What is the secret all of the great saints knew?

9. What is holy reflection?

10. Who is the perfect example of someone who practiced holy reflection?

11. When is it wise to seek the insight of someone who is spiritually wiser than we?

a. __________

b. __________

c. __________

12. What do we call such a person?

Woman of Grace

St. Catherine of Genoa (1447 – 1510)

The life of St. Catherine of Genoa confirms that spiritual renewal, virtue, holy reflection, and spiritual direction lead to wisdom and discernment. Born into an illustrious Italian family that was connected to two popes, Catherine was known as a quiet and pious child, being both prayerful and obedient. She expressed an interest in the convent at the age of thirteen but she was turned away because she was too young.

At the age of sixteen she married Julian Adorno, a nobleman of her parents' choosing. Unfortunately, Adorno proved to be weak in character. He was a spendthrift, violent-tempered and unfaithful. His financial imprudence eventually bankrupted the family while his ill temper robbed his wife of her élan. For the first five years of their marriage, Catherine attempted to obey Adorno, and then for the next five years she turned to the world and the company of frivolous women to console her. The strain of her unhappy marriage coupled with a spiritual life turning lukewarm sent Catherine into a deep depression. Realizing her miserable condition, she prayed for her previous spiritual fervor to be restored and asked the intercession of St. Benedict.

Catherine's turning point came in the year 1473. At the urging of her sister who was a nun, she went to confession to a holy priest. As soon as she knelt down in the confessional, she was overcome both with the wretchedness of her own sin and the immense love and mercy of God. The revelation was so overwhelming that she swooned in an ecstasy. For days, her only utterances were sighs of contrition and sighs of love. Catherine's miraculous restoration of faith took place on the feast of the saint whose intercession she sought, St. Benedict.

The impact of Catherine's experience was profound. Her desire for Holy Communion was an unquenchable thirst; she tended to her home duties with diligence and love and yet spent six hours a day in prayer; she began to devote herself to the poor and sick and cared for them without regard for her own health or well being. Soon, her husband Julian was brought to conversion and then to an active faith, ultimately becoming a member of the third order of St. Francis. Now living as brother and sister, the couple moved near the Hospital of Genoa and devoted themselves to tending the sick. When Julian died in 1497, Catherine provided for his illegitimate daughter, named her in her will, and forgave her husband's mistress. For several years after, Catherine acted in the capacity of administrator and treasurer of the hospital and died in 1510 from an undiagnosed illness. Some say she died of exhaustion of body and soul, consumed by the fires of divine love burning within her.

> *"We should not wish for anything but what comes to us from moment to moment exercising ourselves nonetheless for good."*
>
> SAINT CATHERINE OF GENOA

FAITH IN ACTION

Wisdom is the gift to see all aspects of our life through the eyes of God. St. Catherine of Genoa came to see that even her struggles with her husband could bring great spiritual benefit when surrendered to God. Difficult trials and difficult people are often the "instruments" the Lord uses to bring us to true holiness of life. Where am I currently struggling in my life? What trial is now facing me? What may God be saying to me in the midst of it?

Woman of Grace

Dorothy Day, Servant of God (1897 – 1980)

How does God use the events of our lives to bring us to spiritual renewal and relationship with Him? One contemporary woman serves as a remarkable example. Dorothy Day's young adult life in the 1920's reads like the diary of a 1960's hippie revolutionary. And yet, in a few short years she became a Catholic social justice advocate, deeply in love with Christ and His Church.

Born in 1897 to nominal Protestants, by age eighteen Dorothy was writing for a socialist newspaper called the *New York Call.* An avowed pacifist, Dorothy championed for the poor and oppressed, and advocated the needs of the common worker. She associated with communists and anarchists, and was jailed repeatedly for picketing and protesting for women's rights.

Dorothy had a series of lovers and an illegal abortion; when she did marry she divorced a year later, then moved in with her common-law husband, atheist biologist Forster Battingham, and had his child. It was during this pregnancy that Dorothy became intrigued by the deep faith of many Catholic immigrants, and her empathy eventually blossomed into a desire to enter the Catholic Church. She began to visit Catholic churches, and even prayed the rosary.

When Tamar Teresa was born, Dorothy insisted on baptizing the child Catholic. The couple's relationship rapidly deteriorated, followed by a painful series of separations and reconciliations. Ultimately Dorothy broke it off. Though she loved Forster deeply, she knew their illicit relationship could not continue.

This began a lonely time for Dorothy. On assignment in Washington DC, covering a hunger strike, Dorothy found herself in the National Shrine of the Immaculate Conception. Later, she wrote: "There I offered up a special prayer… with tears and anguish, that some way would open up for me to use what talents I possessed for my fellow workers, for the poor."

Dorothy's prayer was answered when she returned to New York and met Peter Maurin, a French peasant who became her mentor. Peter led a life of voluntary poverty, and helped Dorothy to root her passion for the poor in a Catholic understanding of the human person, and the necessity of personal sacrifice in every work of mercy.

Together they founded the Catholic Worker Movement, which met with immediate success. *The Catholic Worker* newspaper debuted with an initial run of 2,500 copies, climbing to a circulation of 100,000 by the end of the first year. Around the country, intellectuals, uneducated lay people, bishops and clergy rallied around the efforts of this burgeoning Movement. Within a few years, thirty-three Catholic Worker houses and farms had been established to aid the poor and to train students who sought to implement the ideals that Peter and Dorothy had fostered.

During the war years the Movement fell on hard times. Dorothy's staunch pacifist stand was often misunderstood. Peter Marin died in 1949. Sad but undaunted, Dorothy embraced the scriptural mandate to become a saint. Turning one of the Catholic Worker houses into a retreat house, she entered into a deepening life of prayer, and sought to reconcile temporal issues with spiritual values.

In the 1960's, the changing world was a vexation to her. She lamented over the exodus of priests and nuns from the Church, the decline in religious practices among the followers of the Catholic Worker Movement, and the erosion of traditional practices in the Church. In the 1970's, her heart began to fail, yet she continued to travel and write.

Early in the evening of November 29, 1980, with Tamar at her side, Dorothy breathed her last. In the letter to the Holy See to initiate Dorothy's cause for canonization, Cardinal John O'Connor wrote of Dorothy, "Like so many saints of days gone by, she was an idealist in a non-ideal world. It was her contention that men and women should begin to live on earth the life they would one day lead in heaven, a life of peace and harmony."

FAITH IN ACTION

Dorothy wrote: "To work to increase love for God and our fellow man (the two must go hand in hand), this is a lifetime job. We are never going to be finished." How has this been true in your own life?

Lesson One

Wisdom Day By Day

A Prayer of Dedication to Christ

Lord Jesus Christ,
Take all my freedom and my memory,
my understanding and my will.
All that I cherish You have given me.
I surrender it all to be guided by Your will.
Your grace and love are wealth enough for me.
Give me these, Lord Jesus, and I ask nothing more.
Amen.

WEEKLY THEME

Holy wisdom, the ability to see God working in and through all of life's circumstances, transforms our perspective and reveals the eternal value of all things.

WEEKLY GRACE

I pray for the grace of holy wisdom so that I may conform my life to the will of God's good pleasure.

Full of Grace:* *Read pages 105 – 109 in the text, then answer the following questions.

1. In your own words, define wisdom.

2. Specifically, how does wisdom transform our perspective? In what ways have I seen this in my own life?

3. What is God's will of good pleasure and how do we cooperate with it?

4. Relate a time when you exercised conformity of total surrender. To what extent did this cause your faith and trust in God to grow?

KNOW THE FAITH

What Time Is It?

The ancient Greeks had two words for time: *chronos* and *kairos*. *Chronos* refers to time that is measured by clocks and calendars, seasons and years. It refers to the passage of time in seconds, minutes, and hours, months and millennia. *Chronos* is the time by which we set our watches and our schedules.

Kairos, on the other hand, refers to a completely different kind of time. It refers to a moment of great opportunity, a moment in which a critical change takes place. It is the opening in the fabric of life through which a new thread passes that forever alters the tapestry of history. For the Christian, *kairos* refers to God's time — a moment in which the eternal intersects the temporal, changing it forever.

The Scriptures recount many instances of *kairos* moments. A few include:

- The first Passover
- The Israelites leaving Egypt
- The giving of the Ten Commandments
- The Annunciation of the Blessed Mother
- The Incarnation and birth of Jesus
- The institution of the Eucharist at the Last Supper
- The Passion, death, and Resurrection of Jesus
- The day of Pentecost
- The years of Jubilee celebrated by our Catholic Church

While it is sometimes easy to see *kairos* moments in the overall history of human civilization, the great reality is that every day presents us with an opportunity to experience the eternal dimension in our daily lives. This is because our personal history as well as the history of mankind is shot through with the presence of God. God's very name says as much. In Exodus 3, God identifies Himself as "I AM." The *Catechism of the Catholic Church* tells us that this revelation of His Name indicates that He is the "God who is always there, always present to His people in order to save them" (#207). God never abandons His people (see Isaiah 49:15-16). He is always faithful. He is "God with us" (Isaiah 7:14).

The *Catechism* reiterates this fact. It tells us: "God cares for all, from the least things to the great events of the world and its history" (#303). This consoling paragraph assures us that there is nothing about our human situation, nothing about our everyday lives, of which God is not aware: *"Are not two sparrows sold for a penny? And not one of them will fall to the ground without your Father's will. But even the hairs of your head are all numbered. Fear not, therefore; you are of more value than the sparrow"* (Matthew 10:29-31). Our omniscient God is also omnipresent — He is always with His people, providing for them in all things.

Why, then, don't we see these *kairos* moments? According to the Greek philosopher Socrates, "The life that is unexamined is not worth living." To see the eternal dimension entering into our daily life, to discover the hand of God at work in and through all things, we must ponder, we must reflect. This is the example Our Lady gives us when St. Luke tells us she "pondered all these things in her heart." She shows us that *kairos* moments are meant to be grasped — intellectually and experientially.

The hustle-bustle of our contemporary world can obscure the greater realities all around us, and blind us to the truth unfolding within. We must hear with the ears of our heart. We must see with the eyes of our soul. This is the way to wisdom and understanding, to spiritual maturity and hope. Then, just as the life of our Blessed Lady was transformed the moment she spoke her faith-filled "Yes," our *chronos* becomes imbued with *kairos*, transforming both our personal history and the history of mankind by the presence of God.

1. Take a reflective moment and "examine" the days of your life. What are some *kairos* moments from your past?

2. What *kairos* moments might you be experiencing now?

3. Read Isaiah 43:1-12. Mark those words, phrases, or sentences that speak most to your heart. What is God saying to you through them?

WORD TO KNOW

Omniscience: One of God's attributes, meaning that God is all-knowing (He knows all things). Two other attributes related to God's omniscience are omnipotence (God is all-powerful and can do all things) and His omnipresence (God is everywhere).

FOR PONDERING

Wisdom from on High

The Scriptures are full of God's promises. However, many people don't see these promises being fulfilled in their own lives. When this happens, it is often because most of God's promises come with conditions. God will do A, if you do B.

For example:

> *If any of you lacks wisdom, let him ask God, who gives to all men generously and without reproaching, and it will be given him. But let him ask in faith, with no doubting, for he who doubts is like a wave of the sea that is driven and tossed by the wind. For that person must not suppose that a double-minded man, unstable in all his ways, will receive anything from the Lord (James 1:6-8).*

In this passage, God promises wisdom to those who need it. However, to receive this wisdom, two conditions must be met: 1) You have to ask for it. 2) You must not doubt that you will receive it. The "not doubting" part is crucial. When you are talking to a friend or talking to your child or asked to defend the faith, and you don't know what to say, you should pray right then and ask the Holy Spirit for wisdom — for exactly the right words.

Almost immediately an answer will come into your mind. It may be something you read or heard somewhere. Sometimes it will be something you never thought of before. This quiet message is from the Holy Spirit.

Now, you may choose to discount God's answer, saying to yourself, "That can't be right." However, if you don't say anything, then your doubt will make it harder for you to receive God's wisdom again. If you believe and speak out, you will be amazed at the power of your words.

I have taught this verse to many women and challenged them to ask and believe. Inevitably they come back to me and say, "You won't believe what happened. I asked for wisdom and I spoke out and it worked."

Of course, I *do* believe and am not surprised, because I know God keeps his promises.

DO'L

Why do you think God's promises come with "conditions?"

____

____

____

IN CLOSING...

I know [Christ] dwells within me all the time, guiding me and inspiring me whenever I do or say anything. A light, of which I caught no glimmer before, comes to me at the very moment when it is needed.

ST. THERESE OF LISIEUX

Dear Jesus,
Illuminate my way, that I might know which way to go; enlighten my mind,
that I might know the words You would have me speak. Amen.

Lesson Two

The Seed of Renewal: Renewing the Mind According to God's Standard

WEEKLY THEME

Holy wisdom, the ability to see God working in and through all of life's circumstances, transforms our perspective and reveals the eternal value of all things.

WEEKLY GRACE

I pray for the grace of holy wisdom so that I may conform my life to the will of God's good pleasure.

Prayer To Do The Will Of God

O Father! O Son! O Holy Spirit!
O Most Holy Trinity! O Jesus! O Mary!
Blessed angels and all you saints of heaven,
Obtain for me these graces that I ask
through the Most Precious Blood of Jesus Christ:

- *To do always the will of God.*
- *To be always united with God.*
- *To think only of God.*
- *To love only God.*
- *To do everything for God.*
- *To seek only the glory of God.*
- *To become a saint solely for God.*
- *To know well my nothingness.*
- *To know always more and more the will of God.*
- *(Here ask for some particular grace that you desire to obtain.)*

Amen.

FROM "MOTHER LOVE"

Full of Grace:* *Read pages 109 – 114 in the text, then answer the following questions.

1. What is the difference between information, knowledge, and the wisdom of God?

____

____

____

2. What are five essential holy practices that help us acquire wisdom? Briefly explain each.

a. ______________________________

b. ______________________________

c. ______________________________

d. ______________________________

e. ______________________________

3. Which of these holy practices do I participate in regularly? Which new one will I add this week?

____

____

4. Read again St. Paul's words from 2 Corinthians 2: 6-7, 13 -16. What are some of the main differences between the "spiritual man" and the "unspiritual man"? How do we obtain the mind of Christ?

____

____

KNOW THE FAITH

The Sacraments: A Step into Kairos

What is a sacrament? St. Thomas Aquinas, the great Dominican theologian, describes the sacraments as "God's eternal secrets finally revealed in Christ." For him, they are "visible signs of invisible things whereby man is made holy." Echoing this definition, the Baltimore Catechism states that a sacrament is "an outward sign, instituted by Christ to give us grace." Both of these definitions for a sacrament use the word "sign." While signs are a part of everyday life (traffic signs, facility signs, etc.), there is a fundamental difference between them and the "signs" of the sacraments.

The signs of everyday life have no power to *effect*, or cause to happen, that which they represent. But, the sacraments are *efficacious* — they not only *indicate* a spiritual reality, they *make that spiritual reality happen*. St. Thomas Aquinas explains this by saying that the sacraments not only signify, but they *cause*; and *it is by the signifying that they cause.*

A stop sign serves as a good example of the difference between a sign of everyday life and the sign of the sacraments. A stop sign *indicates* that a motor vehicle is to stop. The sign itself simply *represents* the idea of stopping. Drivers are expected to know how to interpret the sign and, hopefully, follow through on what it indicates — stop. If the stop sign were to be *efficacious*, like a sacrament, however, it would not only indicate that the driver should stop, it would jump into the street and, by its own power, physically prevent the motor vehicle from moving. Quite a different thing, isn't it?

What is it, then, that makes the sacraments efficacious? From whom do they acquire their power? Again, St. Thomas Aquinas supplies the answer: the power of the sacraments flows from Christ Himself, from His very life, and most specifically from His passion and death. Their power comes directly from the Second Person of the Blessed Trinity, who, in a completely mystical way, is present in the priests of His Church to Whom Christ has given the authority to act *in His person* (*in persona Christi*). St. Leo the Great puts it this way: "The mysteries of Christ's life are the foundations of what he would henceforth dispense in the sacraments, through the ministers of his Church, for 'what was visible in our Saviour has passed over into his mysteries' (*Catechism of the Catholic Church*, No. 1115).

Thus, every sacrament is laden with the divine life of Jesus Christ, and is a portal of grace through which we become incorporated into His divine life — we immersed in Him, He living in us — and the events of our lives become a spiritual reflection forever marked by His journey here on earth. Neither time nor space can limit the supernatural reality of this incorporation. In a wholly mysterious way, we are drawn into Christ's sacred mysteries and are made part of His salvific work; and Christ, in turn, becomes part of our life's events, situations, and circumstances. The sacraments lift us out of *chronos* and envelope us in *kairos*. They provide for us an entrance into the "eternal now," and the minutes and hours of our life become "supernaturalized" with the divine reality of the everlasting Kingdom of God. (Adapted from Johnnette's book, *Experience Grace in Abundance*, published by Our Sunday Visitor, ©2003. All rights reserved.)

1. In your own words, describe what is meant by the definition of a sacrament as an "outward sign, instituted by Christ, to give us grace."

   ____

   ____

2. In your own words explain how "the power of the sacraments flow from Christ Himself."

   ____

   ____

3. Recall a time when you experienced the *kairos* of a sacrament. Write about it here and thank God for the grace He gave you. How can this remembrance enhance your reception of the sacraments in the future?

   ____

   ____

WORD TO KNOW

Paschal Mystery: Christ's Passion, death, resurrection and ascension into glory. "Paschal" comes from the word "pasch," which refers to the feast of the Passover of the Jews and anticipates the full deliverance won by Christ for the whole human race. The Pascal Mystery is the central mystery of the Christian Faith.

FOR PONDERING

A Key to Wisdom

There is a gift for those who wish to live the spiritual life, a key to treasures I never knew as a Protestant or in my Jewish practice. By receiving this gift, we can unlock the treasures of wisdom and receive not only the *vision* but also the *fullness* of the Abundant Life. That gift is the Sacrament of Confession.

C'mon, Ros. A *gift?* I don't *like* confession! It's humbling, it's uncomfortable, it's awkward, and it's embarrassing. And besides, why do we have to confess our sins to a man? Isn't it Jesus who forgives sins?

Yes, of course. Only God can forgive sins. God, in fact is the only one who can baptize, and confirm, and ordain, and unite man and woman in marriage, and anoint the sick, and become our Food. But He has chosen to do all these things through men, human beings made in His image.

The night before Jesus went to the cross, He breathed on His disciples and said to them,

> *"Receive the Holy Spirit. If you forgive the sins of any, they are forgiven; if you retain the sins of any, they are retained" (John 20:22 -23).*

I don't know how many sermons I heard on that verse as a Protestant. Our Lord's words were said to mean many things. The only thing they *didn't* mean is what they said.

When the priest says, "I absolve you," it is not the priest who says that. It is our Lord Jesus Christ who says that to you through His priest. So too at Mass, when the priest pronounces the words of consecration over the bread and wine — when mere bread and mere wine become the very Body, Blood, Soul and Divinity of the God who created the world and who held it together from the manger — if we could see with our eyes what our faith understands, we would not see the priest. It is *Christ* who says, "This is My Body." It is *Christ* who says, "This is My Blood," through the priest.

In his outstanding book entitled *Living the Catholic Faith,* Archbishop Chaput of Denver wrote:

> *The key to unlocking the richness of the Eucharist and the fullness of the Christian life is the Sacrament of Penance, which prepares the heart to recognize and receive its Savior. The most important single thing any of us can do to grow in Christ, reform our hearts, renew the Church, and change the world is simply this: Go back to Confession, regularly and sincerely. Forgive and seek forgiveness. Everything else will follow.*

I have found that to be the case in my own life. How often is "regularly?" When I came into the Church, my priest said monthly. If you've been going monthly, you might aim for twice a month. Oh, you're going twice each month? For *you,* every week. We can't outdo our Holy Father, Pope John Paul II, who goes to confession daily.

"What if I've been away from Confession for years?" you may ask. *"What if I've been away from the Church?"* God will say to you, *"Come home, dear child. I've already paid for all your sins at Calvary. I came that you might have life and have it abundantly. There is no sin that is greater than my mercy. I will forgive you. I will restore you. I will heal you. And you'll find rest for your soul, and peace, and happiness, and life beyond all you've every known."*

Don't wait…run to the nearest confessor. God will meet you there. God bless you.

RM

Based on Rosalind Moss' discussion of the Sacrament, in what ways do you think the Sacrament of Penance fits the definition of a *kairos* moment?

IN CLOSING…

Oh my soul, when our corrupted nature overpowers, when we are sick of ourselves, weakened on all sides, discouraged by repeated lapses, wearied with sin and sorrow, we gently, sweetly, lay the whole account at his feet, reconciled and encouraged by his appointed representative, yet trembling and conscious of our imperfect dispositions, we draw near the sacred fountain. Scarcely the expanded heart receives its longing desire, than wrapped in his love, covered with his righteousness, we are no longer the same.

ST. ELIZABETH SETON

At Your feet, dear Jesus, I lay my dirty burden down. Give me the grace to leave it there, that my hands and my heart will be free to receive You with joy. Amen.

Lesson Three

Seed of Virtue: Acting Upon God's Grace

A Prayer from the Chaplet of Holy Angels

St. Raphael,
Lead me constantly on the road to virtue and perfection.
Amen.

WEEKLY THEME

Holy wisdom, the ability to see God working in and through all of life's circumstances, transforms our perspective and reveals the eternal value of all things.

WEEKLY GRACE

I pray for the grace of holy wisdom so that I may conform my life to the will of God's good pleasure.

Full of Grace: Read pages 114 - 120 in the text, then answer the following questions.

1. Name the four cardinal virtues and briefly describe each. Why are they called "cardinal," and why are they so important?

   a. ______________________________

   b. ______________________________

   c. ______________________________

   d. ______________________________

2. According to St. Thomas Aquinas, how do the cardinal virtues become "supernaturalized"? What is their effect upon us and upon the world around us?

   ____

   ____

   ____

   ____

   ____

3. Why are faith, hope, and charity called "theological" virtues? Describe each.

   a. ______________________________

   b. ______________________________

   c. ______________________________

4. What one virtue would you particularly like to cultivate? Describe it here in terms of concrete behavior in daily life.

KNOW THE FAITH

The Fullness of Time

For the Christian, time is God's gift to us, the means by which we come to know Him, to love Him, and to serve Him in this life, that we might spend eternity with Him in Heaven. In no manner is this reality more stunningly portrayed than in the incarnation and birth of Jesus Christ, the Second Person of the Blessed Trinity.

Through Jesus, time has a new, supernatural value — it becomes *sanctified. In Jesus Christ, the Word made flesh, time becomes a dimension of God* (Pope John Paul II, *Tertio Millenio Adveniente,* No. 10). As we have seen, one way to enter into this holy and eternal dimension of time is by participating in the sacraments. Yet another way is by living a virtuous life. Charged with the presence of God, the Christian virtues work to sanctify us, and are conduits of grace that sanctify the world each time we put those virtues into practice.

Read the following excerpt from the Apostolic Letter, *Tertio Millenio Adveniente,* written by Pope John Paul II in preparation for the Jubilee Year 2000, and then answer the following questions about it.

1. According to Catholic teaching, what period of time is man given to fulfill his destiny? How does man fulfill his destiny? How do you think the cardinal virtues help him to do this? The theological virtues?

2. Why does time have a fundamental importance in Christianity? How does the liturgical year help to fulfill the Christian duty to sanctify time? In what practical ways can your personal life and family life better reflect these liturgical seasons (think of traditions, decorations, activities, etc.)?

3. Consider the statement, "Charged with the presence of God, the Christian virtues work to sanctify us, and are conduits of grace that sanctify the world each time we put those virtues into practice." Why, then, is living a virtuous life essential to the mission of a woman of grace?

Speaking of the birth of the Son of God, Saint Paul places this event in the "fullness of time" (cf. Gal 4:4). *Time is indeed fulfilled by the very fact that God, in the Incarnation, came down into human history.* Eternity entered into time: what "fulfillment" could be greater than this? What other "fulfillment" would be possible? Some have thought in terms of certain *mysterious cosmic cycles* in which the history of the universe, and of mankind in particular, would constantly repeat itself. True, man rises from the earth and returns to it (cf Gen 3:19): this is an immediately evident fact. Yet in man there is an irrepressible longing to live forever. How are we to imagine a life beyond death? Some have considered various forms of *reincarnation*: depending on one's previous life, one would receive a new life in either a higher or lower form, until full purification is attained. This belief, deeply rooted in some Eastern religions, itself indicates that man rebels against the finality of death. He is convinced that his nature is essentially spiritual and immortal.

Christian revelation excludes reincarnation, and speaks of a fulfillment which man is called to achieve in the course of a single earthly existence. Man achieves this fulfillment of his destiny through a sincere gift of self, a gift which is made possible only through his encounter with God. It is in God that man finds full self-realization: *this is the truth revealed by Christ.* Man fulfills himself in God, who comes to meet him through his Eternal Son. Thanks to God's coming on earth, human time, which began at Creation, has reached its fullness. "The fullness of time" is in fact eternity, indeed, it is *the One who is eternal,* God himself. Thus, to enter into "the fullness of time: means to reach the end of time and to transcend its limits, in order to find time's fulfillment in the eternity of God.

10. *In Christianity, time has a fundamental importance.* Within the dimension of time the world was created; within it the history of salvation unfolds, finding its culmination in the "fullness of time" of the Incarnation, and its goal in the glorious return of the Son of God at the end of time. *In Jesus Christ, the Word made flesh, time becomes a dimension of God,* who is himself eternal. With the coming of Christ there begin "the last days" (cf. Heb 1:2), the "last hour" (cf. 1 Jn 2:18), and the time of the Church, which will last until the Parousia.

From this relationship of God with time there arises *the duty to sanctify time.* This is done, for example, when individual times, days or weeks, are dedicated to God, as once happened in the religion of the Old Covenant, and as happens still, though in a new way, in Christianity. In the liturgy of the Easter Vigil the celebrant, as he blesses the candle which symbolizes the Risen Christ, proclaims: "Christ yesterday and today, the beginning and the end, Alpha and Omega, all time belongs to him, and all the ages, to him be glory and power through every age for ever." He says these words as he inscribes on the candle the numerals of the current year. The meaning of this rite is clear: it emphasizes the fact that *Christ is the Lord of time;* he is its beginning and its end; every year, every day and every moment are embraced by his Incarnation and Resurrection, and thus become part of the "fullness of time." For this reason, the Church too lives and celebrates the liturgy in the span of a year. *The solar year is thus permeated by the liturgical year,* which in a certain way reproduces the whole mystery of the Incarnation and Redemption, beginning from the First Sunday of Advent and ending on the Solemnity of Christ the King, Lord of the Universe and Lord of History. Every Sunday commemorates the day of the Lord's Resurrection.

WORD TO KNOW

Parousia: A Greek term referring to the coming of a royal personage. In Christianity, it refers to the Second Coming of Jesus Christ. The Catechism of the Catholic Church states, "At the end of time, the Kingdom of God will come in it fullness. After the universal judgment, the righteous will reign forever with Christ, glorified in body and soul. The universe itself will be renewed" (No. 1042).

FOR PONDERING

The Value of Virtue

The word "virtue" can sound prissy, or call up images of grim duty. A way of describing virtue that I find attractive and compelling is found in the ethical teachings of Catholic philosopher Dietrich Von Hildebrand. He teaches that virtue is a response to a realm of cherished value. With that in mind, let's take a look at three of the virtues mentioned in this chapter of *Full of Grace*: truthfulness, affection, and justice.

- *Truthfulness:* "Honesty is the best policy" is a phrase that refers only to the utility of being truthful. If you are a liar, no one will trust you and, after a while, people won't give you their business. And yet, the most important reason for being honest is for love of the truth. Honesty is a response to the cherished value of truth, one of the names of our Savior, Who is "the way, the *truth*, and the life." When our words reflect reality (even when it is painful) we can build up relationships of trust instead of wary suspicion.
- *Affection:* Having a desire to touch people is not the essence of affection. True affection comes from a warm appreciation for a person who is close to us, and for all the qualities that makes him or her unique and precious. This love overflows through the body in appropriate touch such as hugs and kisses for children, mates, and close friends. This virtue responds to the loneliness we know is hidden within many who are comforted by our gestures of love.
- *Justice:* This power of this virtue exceeds that of any court of law. The virtue of justice inspires the due response required in every situation of life. One pays a personal debt as the due response to the generosity of the lender. How ungrateful it would be for the one in debt to force the lender to nag him to return the money that is owed! In justice, parents owe their helpless babes elementary care. In justice, children owe aged or infirm parents decent care. An employer should respond to the labor of his or her workers with an adequate wage, for such is the just response.

Good deeds and right attitudes become habits of virtue when they are practiced consistently. Even non-religious persons recognize the value of the cardinal virtues (fortitude, justice, prudence, and temperance) for a peaceful and harmonious society. Imagine the difference in your family, your neighborhood or your city if sufficient numbers of people cultivated them.

RC

Review the various virtues mentioned in pages 116-122 of *Full of Grace*. Which do you think you already practice most of the time? Describe them in terms of response to value.

____

____

IN CLOSING...

We must practice the little virtues. This is difficult sometimes, but the good God never refuses the first grace, which gives courage to conquer self; if the soul corresponds to it she will find that she immediately receives light. We must first act with courage, then the heart is strengthened and we go from victory to victory.

ST. THERESE OF LISIEUX

Dear Lord,
Help me to cooperate with Your grace, that I might die to self and live a virtuous life. Through You I can act with courage, conquer vice with virtue, and go from victory to victory. St. Therese of Lisieux, pray for me. Amen.

Lesson Four

Seed of Holy Reflection: Seeing the Hand of God in Daily Life

A Prayer To Do God's Will

Lord, pour out on us the spirit of understanding, truth, and peace.
Help us to strive with all our heart
to know what is pleasing to you,
and when we know it is your will
make us determined to do it.
We ask this through our Lord Jesus Christ, your Son,
who lives and reigns with you and the Holy Spirit,
one God, forever and ever. Amen.

FROM THE LITURGY OF THE HOURS VOLUME 4

WEEKLY THEME

Holy wisdom, the ability to see God working in and through all of life's circumstances, transforms our perspective and reveals the eternal value of all things.

WEEKLY GRACE

I pray for the grace of holy wisdom so that I may conform my life to the will of God's good pleasure.

Full of Grace: Read pages 120 — 125 in the text, and then answer the following questions.

1. In your own words, explain why wisdom is a "contemplative" gift."

____

____

____

2. The spiritual practice of evaluating our life's events through the eyes of faith will help us attain ______________ ______________________ and will enable us to ______________________________.

3. How did the Blessed Virgin Mary practice holy reflection throughout her life?

____

____

____

4. Ask the Holy Spirit to reveal to you the "stars" in your life, both the brilliant and radiant as well as the hidden and veiled. Write about them here.

____

____

KNOW THE FAITH

The Time of Our Visitation

Luke 19: 41- 44 recounts one of the two times Jesus weeps in Sacred Scripture. He is "going up" to Jerusalem, riding on a donkey, and a great crowd comes out to meet Him. As Our Lord drew near the city, He began to weep as He prophesied: "Would that even today you knew the things that make for peace! But now they are hid from your eyes. For the days shall come upon you, when your enemies will cast up a bank about you and surround you, and hem you in on every side, and dash you to the ground, you and your children within you, and they will not leave one stone upon another in you; because you did not know the time of your visitation."

Here, Jesus foretells the terrible fate Jerusalem would experience in AD 70, when Titus would raze the city and destroy the temple. And, He also gives the reason for the destruction of the city — the failure of its inhabitants to recognize the time of its visitation, "for closing its gates to the salvific coming of the Redeemer." As the Navarre Bible explains, "Jesus loved the Jews with a very special love: they were the first to whom the Gospel was preached (cf. Mt. 10: 5-6); to them He directed His ministry (cf. Mt. 15:24); He showed by His word and by His miracles that He was the Son of God and the Messiah foretold in the Scriptures. But the Jews for the most part failed to appreciate the grace the Lord was offering them; their leaders led them to the extreme of calling for Jesus to be crucified."

Jesus had revealed Himself as the Messiah to the Jews in abundant ways. Even His entry into Jerusalem on a donkey fulfilled an ancient Messianic prophesy: "Rejoice greatly, O daughter of Zion! Shout aloud, O daughter of Jerusalem! Lo, your king comes to you; triumphant and victorious is he, humble and riding on an ass, on a colt the foal of an ass" (Zech 9:9). And yet, the Jews persisted in their spiritual blindness, refusing to believe the Messiah would come as the son of man rather than a worldly king (cf. Mt 13-15; John 12:34-37). They refused to believe that His Kingdom was one that "eye has not seen, nor ear heard" (1 Cor 2:9), rather than an earthly kingdom. Disbelieving, the Jews turned their back on the Messiah, and "wars and rumors of war" (Mt 24:6) followed. Separation from God always leads to disorder, disintegration, and destruction, a lesson the first century Jews discovered in a terrible and devastating way. They missed the time of their visitation and chaos resulted.

The same holds true for us. Every day in countless ways, Jesus comes to us. He comes to us in the sacraments; He comes to us in Holy Communion; He comes to us through Sacred Scripture; He comes to us through the teachings of the Catholic Church; He comes to us through the preaching of the Word; He comes to us through the ordinary, and not so ordinary situations and events of everyday life. The gift of wisdom perfects our spiritual vision and helps us recognize these "visitations" of Jesus, these *kairos* moments which are laden with grace and blessing. Unlike the Jews, who missed the time of their visitation, let us be alert and ready. Let us be vigilant and attentive. Let us be sober and prayerful. Through the practice of holy reflection, let us see Jesus in and through all things, sanctifying our time, and drawing us ever closer to Himself.

1. Cast a backward glance over the last 24 hours. In what specific ways has Jesus "visited" you?

____

____

2. Why do you think that separation from God leads to disorder, disintegration, and destruction?

____

____

3. Using your Bible, go to any one of the Scripture passages mentioned above. Meditate on it and then write below how and why your meditation fits the description of a *kairos* moment.

____

____

____

WORD TO KNOW

Pondering: From the Greek sumballo, meaning "to cast together," from ballo, (throw) and sum (together). This indicates that prayerful pondering requires reflecting on all of the various aspects of our life to see how they come together to effect God's will for us. Therefore, we should ask God to give us the gifts of clarity and wisdom to see clearly, and the gift of strength to respond properly.

FOR PONDERING...

Ponder in Your Heart

In *Full of Grace* Johnnette mentioned by name people who have been stars in her spiritual life. Few of us grow in holiness without the help of loving friends.

Of course, God could have chosen to deal with each of us in a totally hidden and private manner, but contemporary theologians emphasize that God, Himself a Trinity, wants us to image that loving communion in our own relationships. Jesus is head of a mystical Body, not just a single limb. By surrounding ourselves with people whose holiness exceeds our own, we continue to grow in virtue by their example. If we isolate ourselves, on the other hand, our growth may stagnate as we compare ourselves in unhealthy ways with others. For example, I might be tempted to see myself as more spiritually "fit" than I really am; or I may stop trying to overcome a habitual character flaw, even though I still have a long way to go. The Holy Father writes this in *Vita Consecrata:*

"God the Father, through the unceasing gift of Christ and the Spirit, is the educator *par excellence* of those who consecrate themselves to him. But in this work he makes use of human instruments, placing more mature brothers and sisters at the side of those whom he calls. Formation then is a sharing in the work of the Father who, through the Spirit, fashions the inner attitudes of the Son in the hearts of young men and women.

"Those in charge of formation must therefore be very familiar with the path of seeking God, so as to be able to accompany others on this journey. Sensitive to the action of grace, they will also be able to point out those obstacles that are less obvious. But above all they will disclose the beauty of following Christ and the value of the charism by which this is accomplished. They will combine the illumination of spiritual wisdom with the light shed by human means, which can be a help both in discerning the call and in forming the new man or woman, until they are genuinely free. The chief instrument of formation is personal dialogue, a practice of irreplaceable and commendable effectiveness which should take place regularly and with a certain frequency" (No. 66).

While this document applies specifically to those in religious life, this section applies to all of those whose aim is Christian perfection.

Good spiritual friends are Christians who know you well and can encourage you when you are down, and gently admonish you when you are failing. Just the sweet sympathetic smile of such a friend when you are in an uncomfortable situation can make all the difference. That smile is, in a sense, a mirror of the invisible smile of our Lord, Who does not judge us harshly but is saddened to see that we are increasing our own sorrows by following wrong paths.

As I write this I am remembering a choice observation of one such friend, a lay contemplative. He noticed that my letters were full of self-condemnation and tortuous analysis. He once observed: "Someday I hope to get a letter where instead of concentrating on Ronda and her failing, you are writing about how beautiful the love of Jesus is that covers a multitude of sins."

In my experience it is important to be open to the insights that spiritual friends want to offer you, even if you are skeptical. Some of the greatest graces in my life came from simply saying yes to my sister who wanted to pray over me for the anointing of the Holy Spirit, and a friend praying with me to accept Our Lady of Fatima's offer to exchange her loving heart for our own.

RC

To whom do I extend spiritual friendship and how do I do this in my family? Parish? Neighborhood? To what extent do I seek to surround myself with others who are seeking to live a holy life? Why or why not?

IN CLOSING...

"To learn from the Heart of Jesus the secret of love for souls and deep knowledge of them: how to touch their hurts without making them smart and to dress their wounds without reopening them; to give oneself to them and yet reserve oneself; to disclose Truth in its entirety and yet to make it known according to the degree of light that each soul can bear. The knowledge required for the apostolate can be had only from Jesus Christ, by encountering Him in the Eucharist and in prayer."

ELISABETH LESEUR

Dear Lord,
Help me to learn from Your Sacred Heart how to love into life the souls You have entrusted to me. When I receive You in Eucharist or sit before Your Holy Presence or spend time with You through prayer, imbue me with the gifts of wisdom and understanding. May I be used by You as a conduit of Your grace in the ones whom I love. Amen.

Lesson Five

Spiritual Direction: Nurturing the Divine Life Within Us

WEEKLY THEME

Holy wisdom, the ability to see God working in and through all of life's circumstances, transforms our perspective and reveals the eternal value of all things.

WEEKLY GRACE

I pray for the grace of holy wisdom so that I may conform my life to the will of God's good pleasure.

A Prayer To Our Lady of Light

Most Blessed Mother,
Be with me as I approach the Lord this day,
that I may learn to quiet the clamor within my soul,
that I may leave behind my worries and questions,
that I may empty myself of all longing and need
so that I may become attuned to holy silence
and hear what God has to say to me within my heart…
Help me to approach all people in this way,
that I may hear truly what each one has to say,
without inserting myself into their messages, and so
come to closer communion with each one. Amen.

FROM *100 NAMES OF MARY: STORIES AND PRAYERS*

Full of Grace: Read pages 125 - 137 in the text, and then answer the following questions.

1. What is the purpose of spiritual direction, and why should I look for a spiritual director?

2. Using the list of ways in which spiritual direction helps us make progress in Christian perfection (pgs. 130-131) which of the ten do you think would advance your spiritual life the most and why?

3. How does our time with a spiritual direction become a *kairos* moment and a visitation with Jesus? Why is docility a trait we must bring to spiritual direction?

4. What can you do if you cannot find a spiritual director? How many of these means can you use on a regular basis?

____

____

____

KNOW THE FAITH

The Kairos of Friendship

In this lesson, we have seen the value of having a spiritual director who can help us to see the hand of God at work in our lives. A spiritual director is meant to be a conduit of grace through whom God guides us and directs us, leading us in the way we should go. Similarly, all true friendships are to reflect God's own love for us, and we are to be a reflection of God's love for others.

Webster defines "friend" as "a person whom one knows well and is fond of; intimate associate; close acquaintance." But Scripture gives us a fuller and richer definition:

> *A faithful friend is a sturdy shelter; he that has found one has found a treasure. There is nothing so precious as a faithful friend, and no scales can measure his excellence* (Sirach 6:14).

All true friendship rests on charity. St. Augustine writes, "There is no true friendship unless you weld it between souls that cleave together through the charity shed in our hearts by the Holy Spirit."

What specifically characterizes the kind of friendship that "welds" souls together? Aristotle outlined five characteristics of such friendship:

1. willing the friend's good,
2. being glad that he is alive,
3. taking pleasure in living with him,
4. having the same preferences, and
5. sharing in his grief and joy.

St. Thomas Aquinas reduces these five qualities to three: benevolence, mutual love, and community of life. What do these holy attributes mean and how do they affect a relationship?

- *Benevolence:* Benevolence is the cornerstone of friendship and is its foundational element. In Mark 12:28-34, Jesus describes benevolence to a scribe in this way: Loving our neighbor as ourselves is second only to loving God with all our being.

Because we desire only the ultimate good for ourselves, benevolence requires that we desire the ultimate good for our friends as well. From a Christian perspective, this means that we seek the eternal salvation of our friends as we seek our own. Thus, benevolence wills the supernatural good of a friend. Our friendship should be a source of grace for both parties, and the relationship should be a reflection of holiness in the world. True friendship turns away from that which is temporal and fleeting, and toward that which is immortal and everlasting.

Benevolence seeks the best interests of the other, and because of this it dispels willfulness and stubbornness. It dispels envy or manipulation. It dispels selfishness and deceit. It dispels pride and arrogance. Rather, benevolence instills openness and love, faith and confidence, right judgment and joy.

- ***Mutual Love:*** This second characteristic of true friendship is about godly reciprocity. Because true friendship is a gesture of love, it requires a response. In a true spiritual friendship, affection and goodwill must be shared. A friend must be perceived as "the half of my soul," as St. Augustine says.

Sacred Scripture provides us with some beautiful examples of mutual love: Jonathan and David (1 Sam 18-20), Ruth and Naomi (in the book of Ruth), Jesus and Lazarus (John 11:1-44), and Paul and Timothy (1 and 2 Timothy) are just a few examples that show the value and worth of mutual love expressed in true friendship. In them, we see mutual love as the icon of self-donation, the ultimate reality of a God-centered friendship. The following checklist helps us see the quality of our friendships with regard to mutual love:

1. Do we put our friends' needs and wants above our own desires?
2. Are we miserly with our time, or are we always ready to listen?
3. Are we ready to pray with our friend, offer him counsel, or just be present to him when circumstances demand?
4. Do we demonstrate concern for our friends' spiritual well-being?
5. Are we willing to experience discomfort and trial for the welfare of our friend?
6. Do we strive to overcome our weaknesses, failings, and sins in order to become a better friend? Or do we make excuses and assume our friend will "understand?"

- ***Community of Life:*** Without fear of reprisal or judgment, friends share with each other their innermost thoughts and feelings. St. Ambrose of Milan says, "Let us show a friend our heart, and he will open his to us… A friend, if he is true, hides nothing." St. Jerome says, "A friend must speak to his friend freely as to his second self." Such openness of heart is a by-product of community of life.

Essential to community is the concept of "togetherness." It is impossible to maintain a friendship without togetherness, and togetherness requires an investment in time: time spent together in holy conversation, in prayer, and in sharing joys, sufferings, hopes, and dreams. Such community of life spent between friends offers the perfect setting in which to grow together in Christian fidelity and faith. It lays the foundation of mutual trust upon which can then be built the virtues of generosity, long-suffering, compassion, humility, empathy, loyalty, and fraternal correction — all indispensable to true friendship.

True friendship radiates dignity and beauty, love and joy, peace and happiness. It heals the heart, transforms the soul, and breathes life into the spirit. True friendship shines with charity, sparkles with hope, and gleams with faith. It is resplendent with benevolence, mutual love, and community of life. Ultimately, true friendship, woven into the fabric of the heart by the Holy Spirit, becomes the path on which true friends sojourn to heaven together. Thus, time spent with a true friend is laden with *kairos* moments and yields abundant fruit in our life and in the life of our friend as well. (Adapted from *Experience Grace in Abundance*.)

1. How many of your relationships would you say are true friendships? How do these friendships exemplify the three characteristics of a true friendship?

___

___

___

2. Look up one of the famous friendships cited from Sacred Scripture. What impresses you most about that friendship?

3. How do you think true friendships help us to grow in the gift of wisdom? Considering this, why are true friendships full of *kairos* moments?

WORD TO KNOW

Love: The adhesion of the will to that which the intellect presents as good. It is that state in which "correspondence of the wills makes of two one spirit." The Greeks identified four types of love: storge (familial love), philia (love of friends), eros (passionate love), agape (self-donating love without concern for reward).

FOR PONDERING

Direction, Please

I was received into the Church by a circle of friends, all of whom had spiritual directors. And the directors I've had throughout my life have always fit the criteria mentioned in this section of *Full of Grace*. What a privilege.

Nowadays it is hard to find such help, not only because of the shortage of priests, but also because few religious and lay people seem to want to assume this difficult but rewarding ministry. If you don't have a spiritual director, you might ask someone whose Catholic life you admire to try out this role with you. Such a person may be more willing to experiment if you make it clear you don't intend to call them up every night of the week for advice. Usually an hour once a month will provide plenty of direction with "emergency" phone calls in time of special need.

I have found that the best spiritual direction comes from a mentor who is able to observe me in daily life situations, not only in a rectory parlor. I find that God gives such mentors special graces to pinpoint what the real problem is — what I am wrestling with.

One insight came from a spiritual director who was both my godfather and one of my professors. He saw me in many different situations. He apologized for the grossness of the image but said, "You know, Ronda, you are a little like a dog tied up to a post on a long leash. You scamper happily, forgetting life's limitations, until you suddenly feel the tug of the rope, and then you arch up and start squealing."

This humorous analogy helped me understand a key factor of my bad temper. Instead of being surprised and outraged by the frustrations of daily life, I should accept my human condition. When I asked a subsequent spiritual director if he could form me into another Saint Catherine of Siena, he laughed. "God already has Catherine; now he wants Saint Ronda." He was inspired to show me that we don't become holy by becoming someone else, but by letting Him love us in our own personality. He wants to love us into a holier form of ourselves.

At another time in my life, during which I was extremely over-extended, my director suggested to me that besides an hour of quiet prayer every day, I should schedule an hour of peaceful recreation. He was wise enough to remind me that exhaustion is not God's will.

RC

Consider Ronda's statement, "He was inspired to show me that we don't become holy by becoming someone else, but by letting [God] love us in our own personality. He wants to love us into a holier form of ourselves." How does this statement strike you? (Consider your emotional, psychological, intellectual, and/or spiritual response to this statement.)

IN CLOSING...

Woman's soul will profit only if it goes abroad to search and to bring home the hidden treasure which rests in every human soul, and which can enrich not only her soul but also others; and it will profit only if it searches and bears home the well-known or hidden burden which is laid on every human soul ... and its expanses must widen in order to be able to take in what it carries.

ST. TERESA BENEDICTA OF THE CROSS (EDITH STEIN)

Dear Lord,
You have created the feminine heart to see the good in others, and the feminine soul to be a refuge and safe haven for those in need. But sometimes my own heart is too crowded with my own concerns to give space to others. Empty my heart, Lord, and fill it with Your love, so there is room enough to shelter all those You bring to me. Help me to conform to Your holy will, and to be an instrument that aids others to do the same. May Your life in me be a beacon leading many others along the path to spiritual growth. Amen.

Chapter Six

Eucharist: Heart of the Abundant Life

Full of Grace: This week covers pages 139-166 of the text.

The very heart of Catholic worship is the Eucharist—the source and summit of our lives. Jesus has given us everything—because HE is everything, and He has given us Himself, body, blood, soul and divinity. Do our human hearts want to return that love, to give Him all that we are? If you have had even fleeting moments when you wanted to surrender to His consuming love, this chapter will help you move toward that divine union.

LESSON ONE — Come, Let Us Adore Him
LESSON TWO — The Early Church Believed in the Real Presence
LESSON THREE — Preparing to Receive Jesus in the Eucharist
LESSON FOUR — Meeting with Jesus: Eucharistic Adoration
LESSON FIVE — The Healing Power of the Eucharist

Questions to Ponder This Week

- Are there shadows in my life, areas that I have avoided examining, areas that I need to look at with Christ? Can I take them to Him in the Blessed Sacrament?
- How similar is our belief in the Real Presence to the belief of the first Christians? How has the Mass changed? Would the Fathers of the Church recognize ours to be the same Mass that they loved?
- Have I respected my privilege of attending Mass each day if I want to do so? What if the doors of my parish were nailed closed, as they were in Communist nations? What if I could not get to Mass because of persecution or even simple infirmity?

Media Response Sheet

Eucharist: Heart of the Abundant Life

Answer the following questions as you watch the pre-recorded lesson given by Johnnette S. Benkovic, founder of Women of Grace®.

WEEKLY THEME

In an act of total self-donation, Jesus gives Himself to me in the Eucharist. I am to surrender myself to Him as well, completely and without reservation.

WEEKLY GRACE

I pray for the grace to receive Jesus in the Eucharist with faith, with hope, and with love.

1. What must we believe to reap the full spiritual benefits of the Eucharist?

____

____

____

2. In the sixth chapter of the Gospel of John, Jesus refers to Himself as the ______________________________.

3. What caused the first breach in the body of Christ?

____

____

4. "Through the gift of His Body and Blood, our Lord wants to transform us. He wants to ____________________, ____________________, and ____________________. We have only to believe."

5. What affects the spiritual benefit the Eucharist renders in our lives?

____

____

____

6. What are the four characteristics of holy desire?

   a. ______________________________

   b. ______________________________

c. ______________________________

d. ______________________________

7. What are two ways we cultivate humility in relation to the Eucharistic Presence of Jesus?

____

____

8. Name three ways we show respect for the Eucharist.

a. ______________________________

b. ______________________________

c. ______________________________

9. A living faith for the Eucharist is sometimes also called a ______________ for the Eucharist.

10. What is the preeminent grace of the Eucharist?

____

____

____

11. Ardent desire is marked by a______________ of the Eucharist that is interwoven throughout our day.

12. How do we make a spiritual communion?

____

____

____

13. What key to transformation does 2 Corinthians 3:18 give us? What is an "unveiled face?"

____

____

14. What do we call such a person?

____

____

____

Woman of Grace

St. Elizabeth of Portugal (1271 – 1336)

From the womb, Elizabeth seemed chosen by God to be a peacemaker. Her birth itself healed a rift between her father King Pedro III of Aragon and her grandfather. Elizabeth had a pious upbringing, regular religious instruction, and a good education. Mass, Eucharist, and the reading the Divine Office formed the backbone of her prayer life, holy habits she continued throughout her life.

Elizabeth was bright and beautiful, and her family well connected. Many men sought Elizabeth's hand in marriage; her parents decided that twenty-year-old King Dinis of Portugal was the best match for their daughter. At the age of thirteen, the young queen arrived in Portugal to start her new life.

King Dinis was a popular king, known for his hard work and his poetic nature — and for his lax morals. The king sired seven children out of wedlock, while he and Elizabeth had only one son and one daughter. Though deeply hurt by the king's infidelities and abuses, she did not publicly expose the king for his transgressions. She must have voiced her displeasure privately, however, and prayed fervently for his conversion. The king was clearly aware of the great suffering he caused Elizabeth, and penned his thoughts of her in poetic verse: *"I don't know how to justify myself to my lady / Should God lead me to stand before her eyes / Once I'm before her she will adjudge me/ Her betrayer, and with plenty of reason.*

Queen Elizabeth loved and served the poor, building hospitals, convents, orphanages, and other buildings, some of which stand to this day. Every Good Friday, she had a number of lepers brought to her secretly. She would serve them a meal, wash them, dress their wounds, give them clean clothes and fill their purses with money.

Elizabeth's generosity of heart and Christian love led to perhaps her most heroic act of charity. Well aware of his wife's keen intellect and great virtue, the king asked her to care for and tutor his out-of-wedlock children. She did not refuse. Unfortunately, this arrangement bore bitter fruit as her children grew to adulthood. Alfonso, her son, became increasingly jealous and hostile toward his half-brother, and was determined not to wait until his father's death to have the throne. Alfonso led a revolt against his father, and King Dinis responded by reinforcing his own army and banishing Elizabeth to exile, wrongly believing she was siding with her son. The whole kingdom stood in peril as a result of this family feud.

Deeply troubled by this conflict between the two men she loved most, Elizabeth was determined to mediate peace between the two sides. Riding for days, she arrived at the battlefield and rode into the midst of the two armies, and succeeded in negotiating peace between the two sides.

Elizabeth's prayers for the king's conversion were answered later in his life. He reformed his immoral ways, and died a penitent with Elizabeth attending him. Upon the king's death, Elizabeth distributed her personal property to the poor, became a Franciscan tertiary, and retired to a Poor Clare monastery she had founded.

Still, her role as peacemaker was not over. When her son King Alfonso marched against his son-in-law, the King of Castile, to punish him for being an abusive husband to Alfonso's daughter, Elizabeth again rode to the battlefield, now much older and in poor health. This peacemaking mission took its toll on her, however, and she died shortly thereafter. Her body remains incorrupt, reportedly intact, beautiful and in peaceful repose. Pope Urban VIII canonized Elizabeth of Portugal on May 25, 1625.

"Seeing as God made you without peer / In goodness of heart and goodness of speech / Nor is your equal to be found anywhere./ My love, My lady, I hereby tell you: / Had God desired to ordain it so / You would have made a great king.

KING DINIS EXTOLLING HIS WIFE, QUEEN ELIZABETH

FAITH IN ACTION

In what way(s) is Saint Elizabeth of Portugal a good role model for me? How can I best imitate her in my life?

Woman of Grace

Ven. Thecla Merlo (1894-1964)

Meditation on Sacred Scripture and Adoration of the Blessed Sacrament have been the foundation of prayer for many women destined to be great spiritual mothers. Such was the case with Maestra Thecla, first Superior General of the Daughters of St. Paul founded by Father James Alberione. Teresa Merlo was a pious young Italian woman whose family was alive with Catholic piety and devotion. She had been trained as a seamstress but desired to enter religious life. Her brother, a seminarian, introduced her to Father Alberione who was looking to form a feminine congregation dedicated to spreading the Gospel through the press. With faith and trust in God, Teresa said "yes" to Father Alberione's suggestion that she join the group of women he was forming. In 1922 she was consecrated to serving the Lord along with nine other women. This new order, called the *Daughters of St. Paul,* was forging new apostolic ground in the area of mass communications and women religious. Teresa chose the name "Thecla" in honor of St. Thecla, the early follower of St. Paul.

As her name suggested, Thecla was dedicated to the mission she embraced. However, her private letters indicate that she lived with a sense of inadequacy regarding the call entrusted to her, and she suffered from an inability to see God's designs for the future development of the Institute. These spiritual sufferings, however, did not diminish her enthusiasm nor her zeal, rather, they worked to draw her more closely to Sacred Scripture and the Eucharistic Presence. Jesus was the Way and He would lead her and guide her. As she told her sisters, "Our Master dwells in the Tabernacle. From there he preaches to our mind and heart by means of the Gospel...We must always live united to Jesus. The Holy Trinity dwells in those persons who are united to Jesus."

In notes she wrote, Maestra Thecla outlined the three main characteristics of her spiritual life. They provide a spiritual tripod upon which the interior life can rest secured:

1. **Listening:** A simple and life-oriented meditation of the Word of God.
2. **Imitation:** On-going contemplation of Jesus the Master, encouraged by the biblical phrase: "Learn from me for I am meek and humble of heart" (Mt. 11:29). Her resolution was "to imitate Jesus, the Divine Master. To ask myself: What would Jesus do? I want to imitate the Divine Master and become a saint... Jesus Christ is my model. I must fix my gaze on him so as to see how he prayed, spoke, acted, dealt with people; how he willingly suffered for us ..."
3. **To Live the Master:** Imitation of the Divine Master is to lead us to a deeper level of spiritual life. For Thecla this meant "sharing" the Master's life, immersing herself in Him, and conforming herself to Him. Ultimately, this culminates in immersion in the Paschal Mystery, by which the person unites herself to the Master's offering of his life.

"To do good, to help souls, and to contribute to their salvation" were the words Maestra Thecla chose to encapsulate her sense of mission. She was a woman of her time, but a woman whose vision reached toward a new millennium.

(INFORMATION ACQUIRED FROM WWW.DAUGHTERSOFSTPAUL.COM)

> *"One cannot have recollection (an abiding sense of the presence of God throughout the day) if she does not make her meditation.... One becomes nervous; she sees everything distorted; she succeeds in nothing.... We need God. We must be united to Him or else we will not do good."*

VENERABLE THECLA MERLO
FOUNDER OF THE DAUGHTERS OF ST. PAUL

FAITH IN ACTION

In what one way can I most relate to Maestra Thecla? In what practical way(s) do I or can I implement her "tripod" of spirituality?

Lesson One

Come, Let Us Adore Him

Prayer of St. Peter Julian Eymard

O God, Who in a wonderful Sacrament
hast bequeathed to us the memorial of Thy Passion,
Grant we pray that we may so venerate
the sacred mysteries of Thy Body and Blood,
as to continually experience within us
the fruit of Thy Redemption. Amen

WEEKLY THEME

In an act of total self-donation, Jesus gives Himself to me in the Eucharist. I am to surrender myself to Him as well, completely and without reservation.

WEEKLY GRACE

I pray for the grace to receive Jesus in the Eucharist with faith, with hope, and with love.

Full of Grace: Read pages 139 - 143 in the text, and then answer the following questions.

1. How can we become "impregnated by the spirit of the gospel?" Why do you think Pope John Paul II used this distinctively feminine image?

2. Refer to the sixth chapter of John's Gospel, how many times does Jesus refer to Himself as the "bread of life"? What do you think is the significance of this repetition?

3. In this same chapter, what excuses did the Jews give for not believing Jesus? Do you think that believing in the Real Presence is more or less difficult today than it was for the people who lived in the time of Christ? Why do you think this?

4. What is the "true sign of discipleship" suggested in the reading? How does Simon Peter show he is a true disciple? To what extent would you qualify as such?

KNOW THE FAITH

The Holy Sacrifice of the Mass: We Prepare to Receive from God

The Mass unfolds according to a fundamental structure that has been preserved through the centuries. It is comprised of two parts that together form "one single act of worship" (*SC, 70*): the Liturgy of the Word and the Liturgy of the Eucharist (*Catechism of the Catholic Church*, No. 1346). These two parts of the Mass are rooted in the Old Testament, where God's covenant with the Israelites was ratified (cf. Ex 24:7-8).

As we gather and prepare to receive the Word of the Lord, the Mass begins with the opening hymn. This hymn is sung while those with an official ministry to perform process into the Church. In a sense, this opening procession is reminiscent of the Old Testament custom of the bridegroom who processes with his friends to the home of his bride to take her to himself. The priest, who acts *in persona Christi*, comes as the bridegroom with his attendants, to take his bride, the Church, unto himself. Indeed, this is cause for music and song: Jesus Christ, our bridegroom, is come to unite Himself with us, His bride.

When the members of the procession arrive at the altar, they make a solemn bow toward the altar (or genuflect if the Blessed Sacrament is present in the tabernacle), and the priest and deacon (if there is one) go to the altar and kiss it. The altar is kissed as a sign of veneration because it is a symbol of Christ who will make Himself present upon it. The priest and the people then make the Sign of the Cross, a basic but most profound prayer of the Church. Each time we sign ourselves we are reminded of our redemption, of the One who attained it for us, that we belong not to ourselves but to God, and that we are sealed with the Blood of the Lamb. The priest then greets the congregation with a greeting from Sacred Scripture, and the congregation returns his greeting.

Preparation for the Liturgy of the Word continues with the Penitential Rite. This rite helps us to consider the many ways we have sinned against God and the great need we have of His mercy. It reminds us that we are all part of the mystical body of Christ and that our actions, private as well as public, affect all of the members. This time of preparation is especially essential today when so many have fallen away from the sense of sin. The rite of penance most commonly used is the Confiteor, which means, "I confess" in Latin.

The Confiteor takes the form of a public declaration of our sins. It admits that we are all sinners and that we have all fallen short of the glory of God (cf. Rom 3:23). Through the Confiteor we proclaim to God, and to everyone in the Church as well, that we have sinned through our own doing. It is common to strike the breast three times as we admit to our fault. In ancient times, striking the breast was a sign of mourning and we see evidence of it in both the Old and the New Testament (cf. Zech 12:1; Lk 18:13; Lk 23:48). Striking our breast is a sign of sorrow for the sins we have committed.

Next in the liturgy is the Kyrie, which is Greek for "Lord, Have Mercy." Again, the purpose of this prayer is to acknowledge our sinfulness and our need for God's mercy. Like all of the prayers of the Mass, the Kyrie is profoundly scriptural. Throughout the Gospel, we see many sinners crying out to Jesus asking for His mercy, recognizing that He is the One who takes away our sins (cf. Mt 9:27-30; Mt 15:22-28; and Mk 10:46-52).

After the Penitential Rite we sing the "Gloria." This is a song of praise and thanksgiving to the God who saves us, who meets our needs, and who sends His Son to redeem us. This song of praise uses the words the angels sang to the shepherds on that first Christmas morning. It also reminds us of Revelation 4:8, where St. John recounts the heavenly liturgy that never ends. The Gloria is sung at every Sunday liturgy except during the seasons of Advent and Lent. It is omitted during Advent because we are "awaiting" the coming of the Savior. During Lent it is omitted because of the deeply penitential nature of the season.

Preparation for the Liturgy of the Word ends with the Collect, an apt name since it takes all of the prayers we have already offered to God, collects them as one, and presents them to Him. In English, it is often referred to as the Opening Prayer. The Collect consists of four parts: calling upon God, recalling some deed He has done, making a request of Him, and offering the prayer to Him through the mediation of Jesus, His Son. The congregation gives its assent to the prayer by responding "Amen" at its close, and then is seated for the Liturgy of the Word, which we will describe in the next lesson.

1. What are the two main parts of the Mass?

____

____

____

2. What do you think is the connection between repenting for our sins and being spiritually ready to hear the Word of God proclaimed?

____

____

____

3. All of the principal parts of the Mass were in place by the second century. In A.D. 155 St. Justin Martyr delineated for the pagan emperor, Antoninus Pius, what Christians did at their gatherings. Read the account and name all of the parts of the Mass that you recognize.

____

____

____

On the day we call the day of the sun, all who dwell in the city or country gather in the same place. The memoirs of the apostles and the writings of the prophets are read, as much as time permits. When the reader has finished, he who presides over those gathered admonishes and challenges them to imitate these beautiful things. Then we all rise together and offer prayers for ourselves ... and for all others, wherever they may be, so that we may be found righteous by our life and actions, and faithful to the commandments, so as to obtain eternal salvation.

When the prayers are concluded we exchange the kiss. Then someone brings bread and a cup of water and wine mixed together to him who presides over the brethren. He takes them and offers praise and glory to the Father of the universe, through the name of the Son and of the Holy Spirit and for a considerable time he gives thanks (in Greek: *eucharistian*) that we have been judged worthy of these gifts. When he has concluded the prayers and thanksgivings, all present give voice to an acclamation by saying, "Amen."

When he who presides has given thanks and the people have responded, those whom we call deacons give to those present the "eucharisted" bread, wine and water and take them to those who are absent (St. Justin, *Apol.* 1, 65-67).

How has St. Justin's account enhanced my understanding and appreciation of the Holy Eucharist?

____

____

____

WORD TO KNOW

Mass: From the Latin, *missa,* meaning *dismissed* or *sent*. In Latin, the Eucharistic celebration ends with the words, "*Ite missa est,*" meaning, "Go, it is sent." The "it" refers to the Church. The term mass, then, is a reminder that as the people of God we are called to go into the world and bring with us that which we have received, namely, the love and life of Jesus Christ.

FOR PONDERING...

The Lamb of God

I'll never forget the night when, as a Jew, I had dinner in Los Angeles with twelve Jews for Jesus. They claimed the Jewish Messiah had come, and that He was God in human flesh. They told some fantastic tale about His dying on the cross for our sins and rising from the dead to give life to whoever would put their trust in Him.

My companions took me through the Old Testament sacrificial system, and explained that God is a holy God who cannot come into the presence of sin. They explained that the wages of sin is death — separation from God — and that without the shedding of blood there could be no forgiveness for sin. They explained that under God's covenant with Moses, the Israelites would bring a sin offering to the altar. Often, that sin offering was a one-year-old unblemished male lamb, much like the Passover lamb would be. The Israelite would come to the altar with that perfect lamb and place his hand on its head as a symbolic action of identification with the lamb and of his sin passing from him to the lamb. The innocent spotless lamb took upon itself the person's sin and then was slain, its blood shed on the altar as an offering to God for the Israelite's sin.

Now those sacrifices were powerless to take away the sin of the people and they were powerless to change the heart of the sinner. But they were a sign — millions and millions of signs through millions and millions of lambs slain during 1,500 years of the sacrificial system — a sign that pointed to the One who would one day come and take upon Himself for all time the sin of all men, women, and children.

Then, my companions showed me one verse in the New Testament — a verse that is the heart of every Catholic Mass. When Jesus came, John the Baptist looked at Him and said, "Behold the Lamb of God who takes away the sin of the world" (Jn 1:36).

I was shattered on the spot. I thought to myself, "If one little lamb under the Mosaic sacrificial system could take upon itself the sin of a person for a time, what then could the blood of God's Son do on that cross?" I knew then that Jesus was the Messiah and I gave my life to that incomparable Lamb. I became a fervent Evangelical Protestant, the only form of Christianity I knew existed.

Fourteen years later, God opened my heart to consider the claims of the Catholic Church. The Church taught that Jesus meant what He said to the Jews in John, Chapter 6: "Unless you eat the flesh of the son of man and drink his blood, you have no life in you; he who eats my flesh and drinks my blood has eternal life, and I will raise him up on the last day. For my flesh is food indeed, and my blood is drink indeed" (Jn 6:53-55). I finally realized that if the Eucharist is Christ, there is no where else on earth to be but in the Church our Savior established and for which He gave His life, and through which He gives us His very self — Body, Blood, Soul, and Divinity — as our Food.

I began visiting every Catholic Church I could find in every city I visited. And I learned to find the tabernacle in which the hosts were kept, by looking for the little red light that burned as a witness to God's presence. I would kneel before the tabernacle and say, "Is it You, Lord? Are You in there?" He answered me and I will recall for all eternity the night I entered the Church, the night I received the God of Abraham, Isaac, and Jacob on my tongue and into my body, the night I became the most Jewish a Jew could be.

RM

IN CLOSING...

"The Blessed Sacrament is the first and supreme object of our worship. We must preserve in the depths of our hearts a constant and uninterrupted profound adoration of this precious pledge of Divine Love."

ST. MARY EUPHRASIA PELLETIER

Dear Lord,
Give me a burning desire to unite myself to You more fervently through this most blessed gift of the Eucharist, and lead me more deeply into the Sacred Mysteries we celebrate around Your altar. In receiving You, may I become a fount of Your love and mercy in the world. Amen.

Lesson Two

The Early Church Believed in the Real Presence

Prayer of St. Gertrude the Great (adapted)

O Heart, fountain of sweetness!
Give me to drink, unworthy as I am,
of the wine of Thy comfort.
In Thy divine charity raise up the ruins of my spirit,
and out of Thy superabundance of charity,
atone for all the beggary and neediness of my soul.
Amen.

WEEKLY THEME

In an act of total self-donation, Jesus gives Himself to me in the Eucharist. I am to surrender myself to Him as well, completely and without reservation.

WEEKLY GRACE

I pray for the grace to receive Jesus in the Eucharist with faith, with hope, and with love.

Full of Grace: Read pages 143– 150 in the text, and then answer the following questions.

1. *Catena* is a Latin word that means "chain." When used in reference to Church teaching, it means a chain or series of teachings that span from the earliest days of the Church to the present time. From the information given to you in this lesson, create a time line that shows the catena of teaching about the Real Presence of Jesus in the Eucharist beginning with John 6 to the present day.

2. What is the significance of 1 Corinthians 11:23-30 for establishing what the first Christians believed about the Real Presence?

3. According to St. Justin Martyr, who was permitted to share in the Eucharist? Read the *Catechism of the Catholic Church*, 1398 - 1401. How does this correspond to what the Church held in the time of St. Justin Martyr?

4. What one finding of the scientific research conducted on the Eucharistic Miracle of Lanciano most enhances your belief and appreciation of the Real Presence of Jesus in the Eucharist, and why?

____

____

____

KNOW THE FAITH

The Holy Sacrifice of the Mass: The Liturgy of the Word

Sacred Scripture is not just a collection of helpful maxims or good advice, but rather the inspired Word of God given through the evangelists for the salvation of men. Consider these words from the Vatican II document, *Dei Verbum* (Dogmatic Constitution on Divine Revelation, No. 11):

> *Since everything asserted by the inspired authors or sacred writers must be held to be asserted by the Holy Spirit, it follows that the books of Scripture must be acknowledged as teaching solidly, faithfully and without error that truth which God wanted put into sacred writings for the sake of salvation.*

In the *Catechism of the Catholic Church* (No. 104), we read: "In Sacred Scripture, the Church constantly finds her nourishment and her strength, for she welcomes it not as a human word, 'but as what it really is, the word of God' [1 Thess. 2:13]." This consistent teaching of the Church is clearly demonstrated during the Holy Sacrifice of the Mass in the Liturgy of the Word. Here, the reading of Sacred Scripture is central.

The readings of the Liturgy of the Word are arranged according to a three-year cycle during which the entire New Testament is presented to the faithful. These readings are contained in a special liturgical book called a *lectionary* and they are proclaimed from a pulpit or lectern called an *ambo*. This practice finds its roots in the synagogue services of the Old Testament as well as early Church tradition.

The *Apostolic Constitutions*, which dates back to A.D. 400, indicates that reading Scripture was part of the early Eucharistic celebrations. One entry states, "In the middle, let the reader stand upon some high place: let him read the books of Moses, of Joshua the son of Nun, of the Judges, and the Kings and of the Chronicles, and those written after the return from the captivity; and besides these, the books of Job and of Solomon, and of the sixteen prophets."

The Liturgy of the Word is comprised of a reading from the Old Testament, a reading from the New Testament other than the Gospel, a responsorial psalm, and a reading from one of the four Gospels. This pattern varies only during the Easter season, when a reading from Acts of the Apostles is substituted for the Old Testament reading.

The Old Testament reading for Sunday is always related in theme to the Gospel for that day. By carefully listening to the First Reading, we are preparing ourselves to receive the Gospel message God wishes to impart to us for our spiritual growth and edification. In many cases, the Gospel shows us how Jesus Christ is the fulfillment of the Old Testament prophesies and how the Church He came to establish is His Kingdom.

Following the First Reading, a psalm is prayed. The psalm is selected as a response to the Old Testament reading and relates to it in some way. The word "psalm" means "song"; in many parishes the responsorial psalm is sung by a cantor with a repeated refrain sung back by the congregation. This is very much in keeping with the practice and tradition of the early Church.

The Second Reading is taken from the New Testament writings of the apostles. This includes the writings of St. Paul and St. Peter, St. Luke's Acts of the Apostles, and St. John's Book of Revelation. Most typically, the Second

Reading is from the same book of Sacred Scripture for several weeks in a row. Therefore, it is not related thematically to the Gospel as is the First Reading. At the close of each of the Readings, the lector proclaims, "The Word of the Lord," and the congregation responds, "Thanks be to God," another phrase found frequently throughout Scripture.

Though the congregation sits for the readings and the psalm, everyone stands for the proclamation of the Gospel because they are about to hear the words of Jesus Christ. By way of announcing the significance of the Gospel message and in keeping with the solemnity with which the words of Christ are to be revered, an Alleluia (often called the Gospel Acclamation) is sung.

The Gospel readings are bound in an ornate book, which the minister takes from the altar and carries aloft to the pulpit. Two acolytes bearing candles often process with the minister, and many times the Book of Gospels is venerated with incense. All of this reflects the Church's teaching that God is present to us through the words of Sacred Scripture. Just prior to the proclamation of the Gospel, the minister and the congregation trace the sign of the cross on the forehead, over the lips, and over the heart. This is a reminder to keep our minds open to receive the word of God, that we are willing to profess His Word with our lips, and that we will safeguard that word in our hearts.

At the close of the reading, the minister kisses the Book of Gospels and says, "the Gospel of the Lord" to which the congregation responds, "Praise to you, Lord Jesus Christ." Following the proclamation of the Gospel, the priest or deacon gives a homily. A homily is an instruction or interpretation on the Sunday Readings and an application of them to everyday life.

After hearing the Word of God and being instructed in it, the faithful must assent to it. The Nicene Creed, a prayerful listing of all of the essential teachings of the Faith, gives each believer an opportunity to publicly proclaim her belief in God as revealed in Sacred Scripture and the teachings of the Church.

Following the Creed, the Liturgy of the Word concludes with the Prayers of the Faithful. These prayers remind us that we are united in the Mystical Body of Christ. With one voice, the congregation responds to our parish petitions or intentions by praying, "Hear us O Lord," or "Lord, hear our prayer." The Prayers of the Faithful are offered with faith and confidence, knowing that God loves us and desires only the best for us. However, we also acknowledge that He is omniscient, and so we place our trust in His holy will with faith and hope. It is now time to enter into the Liturgy of the Eucharist.

1. Review the First Reading and the Gospel for next Sunday. What theme unites the two?

____

____

____

____

2. Now, look at the Psalm. How does it relate to the First Reading?

____

____

____

____

3. How can I better prepare myself to hear the Liturgy of the Word each Sunday?

WORD TO KNOW

Testament: Another name for "covenant." Covenant, in biblical terms, refers to God's promise to the Chosen People, the Israelites, and brought to fulfillment to all people through His Son, Jesus Christ.

FOR PONDERING

Thicker Than Water

For years, the Iron Curtain separated many families — including mine. Interestingly, when the Berlin Wall came down, there was property in East Germany that needed attending to, and I was drawn into the reunification in my own small way. A home that had belonged to my family was going to be sold, and there was quite a bit of paperwork to take care of, which a cousin stepped in to oversee. I had not heard of this man, who was about fifteen years older than I, and yet he was a close relation. He came to the United States to meet me and to get my signature on some documents.

I remember the day he arrived. I was quite excited, as I had known few blood relations growing up and here was one whom I would meet in just a few hours! I cared nothing about his politics, his hobbies, or his line of work — at the outset I was too absorbed just with meeting a new family member: Cousin Klaus.

A couple of months later I went to Midnight Mass. Having arrived early to get a seat, I had an opportunity not only to participate in the beautiful liturgy, but to spend some time in reflection beforehand. As I meditated on the Incarnation — the mystery of God taking flesh — Cousin Klaus came distinctly to mind. It was then that I understood my deep, spontaneous affection for a man I knew little about: he and I shared a kinship through flesh and blood. At the heart of our relationship that has grown since our meeting was a bond that is, so to speak, "thicker than water."

As I continued to meditate, it became crystal clear to me why Christ chose to enter our world as He did — and more importantly, why He left us the gift of the Eucharist. Only in this way do we share that flesh-and-blood tie that unites families. Only in this way can God, from whom all fathers take their names, be our real Father through the kinship with His Son. The insight has remained with me always. It should also enrich our relationships with other brothers and sisters in the faith — for the Cup we share unites us as well in that flesh-and-blood kinship borne of heaven.

GK

Recall a time when the Mass became a moment of special meaning for you and your family. Write about it here.

IN CLOSING...

"Lord, you have left us your holy Catholic Church as your bride who would tell us about You, her bridegroom, and make Him come alive in us."

—ADRIENNE VON SPEYR

Dear Lord,
What great privilege it is to be a member of Your Holy Catholic Church, for this makes You the Bridegroom of my soul! Draw me to Yourself, my dear Sweet Jesus, and come to live in me as I receive You in Holy Communion. Thank You for Your love and for the gift of faith that unites me to You. Amen.

Lesson Three

Preparing to Receive Jesus in the Eucharist

Prayer Before Communion
(adapted from St. Thomas Aquinas)

Almighty and Eternal God, grant, I beg of You,
that I may receive not only the
Sacrament of the Body and Blood of our Lord,
but also its full grace and power.
Give me grace, most merciful God,
to receive the Body of Your only Son,
in such a manner that I may deserve to be
intimately united with His Mystical Body
and to be numbered among His members.
Amen.

WEEKLY THEME

In an act of total self-donation, Jesus gives Himself to me in the Eucharist. I am to surrender myself to Him as well, completely and without reservation.

WEEKLY GRACE

I pray for the grace to receive Jesus in the Eucharist with faith, with hope, and with love.

Full of Grace: Read pages 150 - 156 in the text, and then answer the following questions.

1. How does the disposition of our heart affect the spiritual benefits we receive from Holy Communion?

2. Of the characteristics that mark a holy desire for the Eucharist, which on do you most need to develop? Think of one practical strategy you can employ.

3. Read the *Catechism of the Catholic Church*, No. 1415 – 1417. What are our obligations toward the Eucharist? What fruits of the Eucharist do we receive?

4. What is a *spiritual communion* and how does it help to produce the fruit of ardent desire?

____

____

____

KNOW THE FAITH

The Holy Sacrifice of the Mass: The Liturgy of the Eucharist

Just as we prepared ourselves to hear the proclamation of Sacred Scripture in the Liturgy of the Word, so too do we prepare ourselves to enter into the most solemn part of the Mass, the Liturgy of the Eucharist. Here, through the actions of the priest, Jesus will re-present to the Father the sacrificial offering of His own Body and Blood in atonement for our sins. Our preparation for this high point of the Eucharist is to offer ourselves, with Jesus, to the Father.

This gift is given to the Father in three specific ways: through the silent intentions of our hearts; through the offertory collection, representing the first fruits of our labor; and through the bread and wine. At the words of consecration, the bread and wine become the Body, Blood, Soul, and Divinity of Our Lord Jesus Christ who, in an act of unfathomable love, offers Himself to us as our spiritual food. As we receive this great gift, a desire is enkindled in our hearts to respond accordingly.

How are we to prepare ourselves to receive this great gift? Making a spiritual offering to God through an interior act of surrender is one fitting way to prepare to receive Christ in the Eucharist. It engenders within us a sense of gratitude and generosity that properly disposes us toward the offertory collection and the communal offering of bread and wine.

While the congregation's monetary offering is being collected, the altar is prepared for the sacrifice. Placed upon the altar is a corporal, a purificator, the Sacramentary, a paten, and a chalice. Just as there may be a procession from the altar to the ambo with the Book of Gospels for the Liturgy of the Word, so there may also be a procession for the presentation of the gifts during the Liturgy of the Eucharist. The gifts of the collection, the bread, and the wine are brought to the altar by members of the congregation, who represent all of the people gathered together for the celebration of the Mass. The priest receives the gift bearers and accepts from them the collection, the bread, and the wine, as well as the gift of self they represent for all those gathered together. He then offers these gifts to God in the name of the assembly and on their behalf.

The bread and wine are placed on the altar, where they are prepared for offering. The wine is poured into the chalice along with a drop of water. The wine represents the divinity of Christ and the water His humanity. The priest prays that all who are participating in this Mass might come to share in the divinity of Christ, who humbled Himself to share in our humanity. The priest then blesses the bread and wine with prayers that are derived from ancient Jewish prayers, many of which are still said today in the homes of Jews during the celebration of the Sabbath. All of the prayers of the Mass find their origin in Sacred Scripture and in the prayer traditions of the Jewish people.

The priest next prays a prayer of contrition and a second prayer that accompanies the "washing of the hands." This second prayer is: "Wash me thoroughly from my iniquity, and cleanse me from my sin!" This prayer is taken from Psalm 51:2, and the accompanying ritual of hand washing comes from the Jewish law of cleansing that preceded a sacrificial offering.

Following the "washing of the hands" the priest invites us to pray with him that God may accept our sacrifice "for the praise and glory of His name, for our good and for that of the whole church." The priest then prays one last prayer before the Eucharistic Prayer begins. It takes together all of the prayers prayed thus far and unites them with a prayer that reflects the special nature of the day. The priest once again asks God to accept the gifts we offer Him through Jesus Christ, and the congregation voices its assent by responding, "Amen."

1. Read paragraph 1098 in the *Catechism of the Catholic Church*. Explain in your own words the role of the Holy Spirit in preparing us to encounter the Lord through the Sacred Liturgy.

2. What are the three specific ways we make a gift of ourselves to the Father during the Liturgy of the Eucharist?

3. Read Paragraphs 1145 – 1149 in the *Catechism of the Catholic Church*. What are some of the signs and symbols we see and experience during the Liturgy of the Eucharist?

WORD TO KNOW

Sacred Vessels: Requisites for the celebration of the Mass that hold a place of honor, most notably the chalice and paten. Other vessels, including the ciborium (chalice-like vessel that holds the consecrated Hosts), the monstrance (the container used to expose the large Host for Exposition and Benediction), and the pyx (the container that holds the large Host in the monstrance) are also considered to be sacred vessels.

FOR PONDERING...

"Lord, I Am Unworthy, Say But The Word And I Shall Be Healed"

What could be more important than meeting Jesus Who in the Mass leaps down from heaven to be with us? No private prayer at home or in a group can compare to this stupendous miracle, in which the Second Person of the Holy Trinity enters our bodies like a lover, to give us grace and strength to live in His kingdom. How happy Jesus is when we are also longing for Him to come into us, so He can lead us further along His path.

More and more Catholics choose to attend daily Mass — some as early as 6:30 AM, on the way to work! Groups of mothers with small children can sometimes car-pool together, and perhaps even persuade a priest to say a Mass for children at least once a week! My choice to participate at daily Mass signifies that nothing on my schedule is more important than the visit of Jesus to my heart. How easily do we experience burn-out from hectic schedules with priorities that need some adjustment.

Going to Eucharistic adoration is also a wonderful way to be closer to Jesus, as is making a spiritual communion. Perhaps you go to Mass but don't receive Jesus in Holy Communion. Or perhaps you do receive, but feel guilty. A priest once revealed in a homily the fact that he lies awake at night, weeping for people who cannot receive. This included those who were committed to sinful patterns of life such as sexual affairs, unblessed marriages, fraudulent business commitments, or contraceptive practices. He begged such people to come to see him so that he could help them change their lives.

Does it seem too difficult to you, to fit in a daily visit with Jesus? Some sacrifice is called for, if we are to receive Holy Communion worthily. A sacrifice is an offering that can be perceived by the senses to show our visible love for God. Be assured that God's grace will be there for you, if you make such a decision.

Other times, people suffer under a false guilt. In some cases a former marriage may be subject to an annulment and your present marriage blessed. Alternatively, it may be possible for a couple with an unblessed marriage to receive communion when the couple is no longer intimate; they may decide to remain celibate, or be incapable of sexual intimacy because of infirmity, alienation, or aging. Make sure you clear away all obstacles that keep you from this essential sacrament.

RC

To what extent am I willing to sacrifice so that I may receive Jesus in Eucharist more frequently?

____

____

____

____

____

____

IN CLOSING...

"How sweet the [Eucharistic] presence of Jesus to the longing, harassed soul! It is instant peace, and balm to every wound."

ST. ELIZABETH ANN SETON

Dear Lord,
How many times have I experienced the healing balm of Your Presence, both in the Eucharist and through Your Word in Sacred Scripture! Plunge me ever deeper into these Sacred Mysteries, that they may produce abundant fruit in my life. Amen.

Lesson Four

Meeting With Jesus: Eucharistic Adoration

Prayer After Holy Communion by St. Blasé (adapted)

Father of mercy and God of all consolation,
Graciously look upon me and impart to me the blessing
that flows from this holy Sacrament.
Overshadow me with Your loving kindness,
and let this divine Mystery bear fruit in me. Amen.

WEEKLY THEME

In an act of total self-donation, Jesus gives Himself to me in the Eucharist. I am to surrender myself to Him as well, completely and without reservation.

WEEKLY GRACE

I pray for the grace to receive Jesus in the Eucharist with faith, with hope, and with love.

Full of Grace: Read pages 157 – 162 in the text, and then answer the following questions.

1. From your feminine perspective, what impressed you most about Father Ronald Lawlor's account? Who has been most influential in shaping your devotion to the Eucharistic Presence of Our Lord?

____

____

____

2. What are the three reasons Pope John Paul II gives us for participating in Eucharistic adoration? Read the *Catechism of the Catholic Church* (No 1418). What three reasons does Pope Paul VI give for adoration of the Blessed Sacrament?

POPE JOHN PAUL II:	POPE PAUL VI:
a. ________________	a. ________________
b. ________________	b. ________________
c. ________________	c. ________________

3. In your *Catechism*, read No. 1379. What was the original purpose of the tabernacle? How has that purpose evolved?

____

____

____

4. In the text we read of some benefits of Eucharistic adoration that others have experienced. What blessing(s) have you experienced as a result of adoration of the Blessed Sacrament?

____

____

____

KNOW THE FAITH

The Holy Mass: The Eucharistic Prayer

The term "Eucharistic prayer" comes from the Greek term, *anaphora,* which literally means "elevation," or "lifting up." The Greek name tells us something important about this part of the Mass — it is the high point, the key moment; it is the very heart of the Eucharistic celebration.

The Eucharistic prayer contains the essential elements of the preface: the *Sanctus*, epiclesis, institutional narrative, anamnesis, intercessions, and *Great Doxology*. Evidence of this outline for the Eucharistic Prayer dates back to AD 215; the formal liturgical texts and settings, such as we use today, were developed as early as the fourth and fifth centuries.

The *preface* is a prayer of preparation for the great moment of Consecration. Like many of the prayers of the Mass, the preface is rooted in the Jewish tradition, specifically two forms of prayer called the *berakah* (acknowledgment, blessing, and praise) and *todah* (thanksgiving). The *Catechetical Lectures* of St. Cyril of Alexandria (AD 350) give us insight into the ancient roots of the preface and what the intention is behind the words we pray:

> *The priest cries out, "Lift up your hearts!" For in this most solemn hour it is necessary for us to have our hearts raised up with God, and not fixed below, on the earth and on earthly things. It is as if the priest instructs us at this hour to dismiss all physical cares and domestic anxieties, and to have our hearts in heaven with the benevolent God. Then you answer, "We have lifted them up to the Lord," while he is preoccupied with physical cares.*
>
> *Then the priest says, "Let us give thanks to the Lord." Certainly we ought to give thanks to God for having invited us, unworthy as we are, to so great a gift; for God having reconciled us to Himself when we were His enemies; for having made us His adopted sons by the Spirit. Then you say, "It is right and just:" for in giving thanks, we do a worthy thing, something that is justice itself. But what God did in accounting us worthy of such benefits was not justice, but much more than just (848d, 848e).*

The preface continues as the priest gives thanksgiving to God the Father for His many blessings.

The next major prayer of the preface is the *Sanctus,* which comes from a prayer the Jews prayed every day in the synagogue during the time of Christ (see Isaiah 6:3). It has several special meanings. *Sanctus* is Latin for "holy," a word that is repeated three times at the beginning of the prayer. In Hebrew, there are no superlatives such as "good," "better," and "best." So, to express the superlative, a word would be repeated. Three repetitions indicated the greatest or highest degree. The *Sanctus,* then, expresses the infinite holiness of God as we pray, "Holy, holy, holy is the Lord."

The rest of the prayer is taken from Mark 11:9-10, which uses the word *Hosanna,* meaning "Save us" (Psalm 118:25). This word reminds us that this is a song of praise in thanksgiving for the gift of Jesus Christ and His saving act for us. The *Sanctus* also reminds us that the Mass is an eternal moment that transcends time and space as our praise is united with "a great cloud of witnesses" who surround the heavenly throne, crying out "Holy, holy, holy, is the Lord God Almighty" (Revelation 4:8).

Most typically, the congregation kneels after praying the *Sanctus*. This emphasizes that we are about to enter into the most sacred part of the Mass, the Consecration. Kneeling also draws our attention to the altar of sacrifice and the holy actions of the priest, who is about to invoke the power of the Holy Spirit. He joins his hands together, palms down, and holds them outstretched over the offering. He asks God the Father to send His Spirit to sanctify these gifts. He then makes the sign of the cross over the bread and wine and beseeches the Father to let them become the Body and Blood of our Lord, Jesus Christ. This prayer, with its accompanying actions, is called the *epiclesis* (Greek for "invoke upon"; see CCC 1353). It is now nearly time for the Consecration, the high point of the Holy Mass.

1. What does the quote from St. Cyril tell us is the reason for the early prayers of the preface?

____

____

2. Look up Isaiah 6:3 and Mark 11:9-10. Write the words that relate to the *Sanctus* in the space provided.

____

____

3. Ponder the fact that the Holy Sacrifice of the Mass is an "eternal moment." What does this mean to you, and what insights have you gained from your pondering?

____

____

WORD TO KNOW

Transubstantiation: A term first used in 1079 to counter misunderstandings about the Eucharist. Linguistically, the word means "the transition of one thing into another in some aspect of being" (or "What was formerly A is now B"). Theologically speaking, the word refers to the change of bread and wine completely into the Body, Blood, Soul, and Divinity of Christ, regardless of its outward appearance.

FOR PONDERING...

A Foretaste of Heaven

I am glad that the practice of Eucharistic adoration is becoming more common. There was a time after the Second Vatican Council when the practice was neglected. Because of this, my children grew up without attending Adoration of the Blessed Sacrament. So one Friday afternoon I convinced my son, then a junior in college, to accompany me to Benediction.

As we walked into our rather plain modern church, the afternoon sunlight streamed through the stained-glass windows, turning the mostly empty pews to gold and red, purple and blue. The incense rose through the sunlight and shadow into the cupola, and the sweet aroma filled the air. On the altar the candles flickered and in the center of an immaculate white lace altar cloth, a baroque golden sunburst held the Blessed Sacrament.

The priest, in a beautifully embroidered cope, knelt before the altar and a small group of women had just begun to chant the *Tantum Ergo*. It was as though we had walked into heaven.

My son turned to me, "Why has the Church hidden this? Don't they understand this is what my generation needs?"

As a film major involved in the arts, he understood the importance of the visual and sensual images. Words aren't enough. People, especially young people, need to be appealed to through all their senses. They have a natural urge to adore, and that instinct should be directed toward God, the only Person truly deserving of such adoration.

Adoration comes more naturally when the surroundings — the architecture, the tabernacle, the altar, the music, the lighting — draw the soul toward adoration. Our churches should be designed so that when we come into the presence of the Blessed Sacrament, we feel as though we are peeking into heaven. True, as long as there is a real priest saying the words of consecration and real bread and wine, Christ is truly present in the Blessed Sacrament. And yet, we must not treat this most amazing gift of God as just ordinary bread and wine. Everything should give glory and honor to the One who lowered Himself, that He might to come to us in humble form.

DO'L

Gnosticism is an ancient heresy that teaches, among other things, that all matter is a corruption of the divine. How does this contradict the Incarnation of Jesus Christ, His teachings, the Eucharistic Presence, and the use of our senses in prayer and liturgy?

____

____

____

IN CLOSING...

"O God hidden in the prison of the tabernacle! I come with joy to you each evening to thank you for the graces you have given me. I ask pardon for the faults I committed today... I offer you every beat of my heart as so many acts of love and reparation and I unite them to your infinite merits. I beg you, O my Divine Bridegroom, to be the Restorer of my soul... Tomorrow, with the help of your grace, I will begin a new life in which each moment will be an act of love and renunciation."

ST. THERESE OF LISIEUX

Dear Lord, Make these words of St. Therese my own, and give me a deep zeal for Your Eucharistic Presence. Vivify me with Your own Body and Blood, restore me and make me new, and ultimately lead me to everlasting life with You. Amen.

Lesson Five

The Healing Power of the Eucharist

Act of Thanksgiving

From the depths of my heart I thank You, dear Lord,
for Your infinite kindness in coming to me.
I thank You for nourishing my soul
with Your Sacred Body and Precious Blood.
Grant that I may spend the hours of the day gladly
working with You according to Your will.
Amen.

FROM *THE GOLDEN BOOK OF PRAYERS*

WEEKLY THEME

In an act of total self-donation, Jesus gives Himself to me in the Eucharist. I am to surrender myself to Him as well, completely and without reservation.

WEEKLY GRACE

I pray for the grace to receive Jesus in the Eucharist with faith, with hope, and with love.

Full of Grace: Read pages 162 - 166 in the text, then answer the following questions.

1. What healing does God most desire to give us, and why?

2. How do I respond to the Eucharistic Presence? Do I see and believe in its healing power? Why or why not?

3. Read in the *Catechism* No. 1393 – 1395. In what way do these paragraphs speak of healing? How have I experienced this in my own life?

4. What does it mean to be a "Eucharistic people?"

KNOW THE FAITH

The Mass: Consecration and Holy Communion

The Second Vatican Council teaches that the Eucharist is "the source and summit of the Christian life" (*Lumen Gentium*, No.11). Jesus instituted the Eucharist at the Last Supper as the means through which His sacrifice on the cross would be perpetuated until He comes again.

Pope John Paul II instructs that the Eucharist is the *gift par excellence* because it is Christ's gift of Himself, His person in His sacred humanity (*Ecclesia de Eucharistia*, No. 11). This *gift par excellence* is given to us at the Consecration of the Mass, when the bread and wine become the Body, Blood, Soul, and Divinity of Jesus Christ.

The Consecration begins with the *institutional narrative*: a retelling of what Jesus did when He instituted the Eucharist at the Last Supper. These Scriptural words are *efficacious*. This means that when the priest says them they have the power, through the Holy Spirit, to bring about the very reality of which they speak. Thus, when the priest says the words of Our Lord, "*Take this, all of you, and eat it: This is my body...*," and "*Take this, all of you, and drink from it: This is the cup of my blood...Do this in memory of me*," Jesus becomes fully present, Body, Blood, Soul and Divinity, in each of the species.

Greater insight into this mystery comes from understanding the Jewish Passover, which commemorates the Israelite liberation from Egypt (see Exodus 12). For the Jew, this "remembrance" is much more than a simple reminder of some past event. In the context of the paschal ceremony, to "do in memory of" or to do "in remembrance of" means to re-present or to make present *now*. Thus, for the Jew, every Passover meal is that first Passover meal. When Jesus changes the bread and wine into His Body and Blood and tells the apostles to "do this in memory of me," it is with this Jewish understanding that He does so. At the same time, He is passing on to the apostles, the first priests, His own power to change the bread and wine into His own flesh. Thus, He is instituting the priesthood and the line of apostolic succession.

Another insight comes from an understanding of the paschal lamb. During the Passover ceremony, a spotless lamb is sacrificed to God as a sin offering on behalf of the Jewish people. The lamb is then eaten at the Passover meal, as it was just before the Israelites fled from Egypt. At the Last Supper, Jesus began the final fulfillment of the Old Covenant, becoming Himself the Paschal Lamb. As both victim and priest, He offers Himself to the Father to "take away the sins of the world" and to give Himself as the Perfect Food to be eaten *for all time*.

Henceforth, no ordinary lamb would be slain as a sin offering, but rather the very Lamb of God! Now, freedom would be won not from a political oppressor, but from the ultimate oppression of sin and death! Every time a validly ordained Catholic priest pronounces the words of consecration in "memory" of Jesus Christ, Calvary becomes present, and the sacrificial offering of Our Savior's Body and Blood is made available to us at that very moment! Every Catholic Mass, then, is that first Mass offered by Jesus Himself! How remarkable!

A word of explanation, however. This does not mean that Jesus is being sacrificed again. As Scripture says, Christ died "once for all" (Hebrews 10:10). What it does mean, on the other hand, is that Christ's sacrifice of Himself on Calvary happened in an eternal moment, and in some mystical way we are present to it every time the Holy Mass is celebrated.

After the great moment of consecration, three final prayers follow. The first prayer is called the *anamnesis* or memorial, and it includes the "Mystery of Faith" (*Mysterium Fide*), an acclamation that states Jesus is the cause of our salvation and He will come again. "Christ has died, Christ is risen, Christ will come again" proclaims one of the four acclamations that can be used. The priest then prays the *memorial prayer* to God the Father. This prayer commemorates the death and resurrection of Jesus and the celebrant asks the Father to look favorably upon the gifts we are offering Him. The third prayer is the *intercessions*. This prayer reminds us that we are not praying alone. Indeed, the whole Church, including the Communion of Saints, prays with us. Thus, we commemorate the living (some of whom are remembered by name such as the pope and the local bishop), and the dead.

The *Great Doxology* (Greek for "word of praise") concludes the Eucharistic prayer. The priest raises the Body and Blood of Our Lord and says, *"Through him, with him, and in him, in the unity of the Holy Spirit, all glory and honor is yours, almighty Father, for ever and ever."* The faithful respond to this doxology with the "Great Amen," thereby signifying again their belief in the Real Presence of Jesus in the Eucharist.

As the Eucharistic Prayer ends, the Communion Rite begins. The congregation prays the prayer Jesus taught us, the Our Father (see Matthew 6:9-13). At Mass the Our Father ends with a doxology that comes from the *Didache*, an ancient book called "The Teachings of the Twelve Apostles," which was written before the end of the second century. It follows a short prayer in which the priest asks God for His continued help and assistance for all of us until Jesus comes again.

The priest offers the congregation the peace of Christ and the congregation, in turn, extends it to one another in the Sign of Peace, which communicates unity and brotherhood. In the United States, the Sign of Peace is most commonly expressed with a handshake. The priest then breaks the bread (Luke 24:30-31), and his attendants prepare the consecrated bread and wine to be distributed. While this is happening, the congregation sings or says the *Agnus Dei* (Lamb of God), a prayer of petition that asks the Lamb of God to have mercy on us and to grant us peace.

As the priest prepares to receive Communion, he co-mingles the bread and wine by breaking off a small portion of the consecrated host and placing it inside the chalice with the consecrated wine. He prays a silent prayer to the Father, asking that the Eucharistic Presence will bring us to eternal life, and then he prays another silent prayer asking for His own sanctification. He genuflects, raises the host slightly over the paten and, facing the people, presents the Lamb of God to all "who are called to his supper." Acknowledging our unworthiness to receive so great a gift as well as our need for it, the congregation responds with a prayer taken from Luke 7:6-7: "Lord, I am not worthy."

The priest consumes the sacred species, and all members of the Catholic Church who are of age and in the state of grace come forward to receive Holy Communion. Prior to receiving, we are given the opportunity to again state our belief in the Real Presence of Jesus. When the minister of communion says to us, "the Body of Christ" and "the Blood of Christ," we once again respond, "Amen," after offering a sign reverence before the Real Presence of Jesus Our Lord.

Following communion, there is a time of meditation before the Concluding Rite. The priest prays a closing prayer of thanksgiving, tells us to go in peace, and sends us out to live what we have just experienced: *Ite missa est.* Then, the Mass ends as it began — the priest kisses the altar, he and his attendants face the altar and bow toward it, and they process out of the sanctuary. When they have exited, and the closing hymn is sung, we, too, exit the church ready to fulfill the great commission after we have taken time to pray a prayer of Thanksgiving for the *gift par excellence* we have received.

1. Why do you think the Eucharist is "the source and summit of the Christian life?"

___

___

___

2. In your *Catechism*, read paragraphs 1575 and 1576. What is "apostolic succession"?

___

___

___

3. How can pondering the reality of the "eternal moment" of the Consecration increase the fervency of our reception of Holy Communion?

____

____

____

____

WORD TO KNOW

Rubric: From the Latin word ruber, meaning red. They are the rules, often printed in red, that govern the conduct of the services of the Church and the ministration of liturgical rites.

FOR PONDERING...

Eternal Healing

We live in a world where religion is perceived to be a matter of personal taste, or a man-made story that we accept because it makes us feel good. If that were true, why bother?

But it isn't. There is a real God, the Holy Trinity. The Second Person of the Trinity really did become man, die for our sins, rise again, and is really present in the Blessed Sacrament.

Jesus said, "Whoever eats My flesh and drinks My blood has eternal life and I will raise him to life on the last day." And when Jesus said, "My body is real food" (John 6:55), He meant it. A lot of people who heard this were shocked and stopped following Him. If He hadn't meant it, He would have explained what He did mean.

The ordinary bread and wine become the Body and Blood of Jesus only when a properly ordained priest says the words of consecration. I could talk to a loaf of bread all day and it would still just be bread. To become a priest you must have hands laid on by a real bishop. Jesus laid hands on His apostles and they in turn consecrated others to be priests and bishops by laying hands on them. And so, from hand to hand, from Jesus to the apostles to the bishops to each priest down through the centuries, the power to consecrate has been passed in an unbroken chain.

The Catholic Church isn't a human institution that can be changed by the will of men. It is designed by God to be the means by which Jesus can become present to us in the Blessed Sacrament. It is the body of Christ present in the world for the salvation of men.

When we kneel before the tabernacle, when we receive Holy Communion, we acknowledge the awesome reality that God, who made the heavens and earth, the ruler of all that is and was and is to come, chose to come and dwell in our church — to be food for our souls.

DO'L

In his apostolic letter, *Mane Nobiscum Domine* ("Stay With Us, Lord," No.25), Pope John Paul II writes, "...the Eucharist is a mode of being, which passes from Jesus into each Christian, through whose testimony it is meant to spread throughout society and culture. For this to happen, each member of the faithful must assimilate, through personal and communal meditation, the values which the Eucharist expresses, the attitudes it inspires, the resolutions to which it gives rise."

Ponder the Eucharist as *a mode of being*. What does that mean to me? How does Pope John Paul II say this can happen? Specifically, how can I cooperate with these words so that the Eucharist becomes my *mode of being?* How, then, can this lead to healing for me and for the world?

IN CLOSING...

"After I enter the chapel I place myself in the presence of God and I say to him, 'Lord, here I am; give me whatever you wish.' If he gives me something, then I am happy and I thank him. If he does not give me anything then I thank Him nonetheless, knowing as I do, that I deserve nothing. Then I begin to tell Him of all that concerns me, my thoughts, my distress, and finally, I listen to him"

ST. CATHERINE LABOURE

Dear Lord,
St. Catherine gives us five steps to adoring You in Your Eucharistic Presence and after I consume You in Holy Communion. Help me to follow her counsel, that I might experience the fullness of life that You desire for me. Amen.

Chapter Seven

Resurrection: Made New for the Abundant Life

Full of Grace: This week covers pages 167-193 of the text.

Resurrection life is a new life in Christ. Is it any wonder, then, that the Risen Christ first appeared to women, who by God's design, are uniquely capable of bearing new life into the world? Mary Magdalene witnessed the message of the Resurrection and its cosmos-shattering truth that Death had been defeated, for "He is not here; he is risen" (Mk 16:6). In Christ, all things are made new (Rev 21:5).

Mary Magdalene rushed to give the good news to the apostles and disciples. The joyous urgency in her voice rings down the millennia, "I have seen the Lord!"

This message is no less urgent today, and women are called once more to witness to the power of the Resurrection. Just as the wounds of His Passion and death could not hold Jesus in the tomb, neither must we allow our own woundedness to keep us from victorious living. There is still sin in the world, but when we live in the healing light of Christ's love for us, we "can do all things in Christ" (Phil 4:13).

Women are uniquely designed to strive for wholeness. Part of the "feminine genius" that John Paul II has perceived for our time is that women in particular will renew the culture. It is our desire to unite our families, our communities. This work is only done first in the heart. Only a heart reconciled to God is a heart that is capable of reconciling others. As you work through these pages take care to submit to the gentle hand of the Doctor of Souls. Your healthy heart will overflow with Christ's love and mercy, renewing your family, your parish, and your community.

LESSON ONE — Healing for the Wounded Heart
LESSON TWO — Identifying the Wounds of the Heart
LESSON THREE — Obstacles to Inner Healing
LESSON FOUR — Lack of Forgiveness: The Greatest Obstacle of All
LESSON FIVE — Two Stories of the Power of Forgiveness

Question To Ponder This Week

- How does allowing God to heal old hurts increase my ability to help others?

Media Response Sheet

Resurrection: Made New for the Abundant Life

Answer the following questions as you watch the pre-recorded lesson given by Johnnette S. Benkovic, founder of Women of Grace®.

WEEKLY THEME
God wants to heal the wounds of my heart. Women of Grace can receive true healing by embracing the graces available to us in the life of the resurrected Christ.

WEEKLY GRACE
I pray for the grace to see the wounds of my heart and to surrender them to the healing love of God.

1. What two things cause our hearts to "leak out" the love of God?

____

____

2. What two things may "flood to the surface" in our time of study and discussion this week?

____

____

3. God wants to heal us. What must we do to be healed?

____

____

4. What does Jesus say in Revelation 21:5?

____

____

5. Where does the memory store our pain?

____

____

6. St. Ignatius tells us a ______________ ______________ helps us to "wage a war" against the sins we commit often.

7. What do we do "on the spot" when we have failed?

____

____

8. What can feelings of unhappiness be rooted in?

____

____

9. Who can help us when we have exhausted the natural and spiritual means of dealing with problems?

____

____

10. Why do people sometimes deny they need to be healed?

____

____

11. How do we exercise faith with regard to healing?

____

____

12. What is the greatest obstacle to healing?

____

____

13. What happens when we do not forgive "those who trespass against us?"

____

____

14. Forgiveness is a ______________ ______________ prompted by ____________________,

which sets us free from the ____________________ of sin.

15. What speeds our recovery process along?

____

____

Woman of Grace

St. Margaret of Cortona (1247 – 1297)

Few would expect that a young cavalier's mistress would one day become a canonized saint of the Catholic Church. But then, few recognized the great love this woman possessed, or the transforming power of that love once she had given her life to God.

Margaret of Cortona was born in Loviana, Tuscany, the daughter of a poor farmer. She was seven when her mother died, and two years later her father married a woman who treated her harshly. Rejected and craving affection, Margaret ran away from home with a young knight who persuaded her to live with him in Montepulciano. She bore him a son and lived as his mistress for nine years, scandalizing the townspeople as they flaunted their illicit liaison. Margaret often entreated her lover to marry her; while he never dashed her hopes altogether, neither did he give in to her pleas.

One day, the cavalier failed to return home. When his dog arrived without him, Margaret followed the animal and discovered her lover's mangled body in a shallow grave, the apparent victim of a murderous band of brigands. Margaret saw in her lover's death the judgment of God. Full of remorse and fear, she gave all her possessions to the cavalier's family, took her son, and returned to her father's house. When the stepmother refused them, Margaret and her son went to the Friars Minor of Cortona, who helped to care for them.

For three years Margaret was plagued with temptations, and her need for affection occasionally induced her to fall back into sin. However, with each transgression she felt a deep sense of self-loathing as well as a desire to repent through harsh and abusive means. More than anything, Margaret wanted to be reconciled to God, but was sure that her sins were too great an obstacle to attain that union with Him.

The Franciscans proved to be spiritual fathers to Margaret during this time of struggle. They helped to moderate her penances and led her in the way of prayer. Under their guidance and direction, Margaret began to make spiritual progress.

A sullied reputation is not easily restored. Though Margaret became known for her works of mercy among the sick and the poor, her former way of life haunted her. Many of the townspeople were suspicious of her and she was often the subject of unfounded, vicious gossip. However, after three years the friars saw that Margaret's conversion was real and they accepted her as a tertiary of their order. At this point, her spiritual life grew to a new level of intimacy with the Lord and she began to receive many spiritual favors, including ecstasies during which she was in direct communion with the Lord.

Margaret's grown son had entered the Franciscan novitiate, and Margaret petitioned the bishop to let her establish a hospital for the sick and poor. Her nursing staff consisted of a group of like-minded laywomen whom she formed into a community she called the "Poverelle" (Poor Ones).

Margaret's last days were sanctified by many miracles of healing and conversion. She led many hardened sinners to repentance even as she continued to lead a life of intense penitence. She died at the age of fifty on the day the Lord had revealed to her in prayer. Her body is incorrupt and lies in a glass-sided reliquary under the main altar of the Basilica of Cortona, which is named in her honor.

FAITH IN ACTION

St. Paul refers to a "thorn in the flesh" that was a source of aggravation and struggle in his life. Have you ever struggled with a recurring temptation or character flaw? Why doesn't God simply remove the attraction from us, so we are no longer tempted to sin? What might God be trying to teach us in our struggle?

Woman of Grace

St. Josephine Bakhita (1869 – 1947)

It is natural to express thanksgiving for being released from difficult trials and circumstances. But who would be grateful for those who *cause* such difficult trials or circumstances? This is the stuff of saints — the very stuff of which Saint Josephine Bakhita was made.

No one knows her real name. The horrific brutality she had experienced at the hand of slave-traders caused her to forget the name she had been given by her parents. The first trader snatched her as she took a short walk from her home when she was only nine years old. Poking a knife in her side, he threatened to kill her if she made any trouble. The slave-trader shackled her to a group of three or four other little captives and led them off into the African forest. When the shackles were temporarily removed so they could eat, the children fled through the forest, only to be ensnared by a second slave-trader at whose home they had sought asylum. *Bakhita,* which means "fortunate," was the name given to her by the second slave-trader.

Bakhita was taken to the markets in Obeid and Khartoum, and sold again and again. Through the years she was subjected to all of the humiliations, beatings and tortures associated with slavery. One gruesome and painful suffering she was subjected to was a custom called "marking." Bakhita was tied to stakes in the ground while intricate patterns were cut into her flesh with a knife and a razor. Salt was poured into the cuttings to prevent them from closing. Flour was then caked into the open wounds so that the pattern would be exposed as a contrast against her dark flesh. One hundred and fourteen patterns were carved into Bakhita's arms, breasts and abdomen. Lying in a pool of blood and overcome with pain and agony, Bakhita fell in and out of consciousness, certain that she would die. About that experience she later said, "I can truly say that it was a miracle I did not die, because the Lord had destined me for greater things."

Eventually, Bakhita was purchased by an Italian consul named Calisto Legnani who treated her with dignity and respect. He took Bakhita to Italy with him and placed her in the home of friends, who were expecting a new baby. After the child was born, Bakhita stayed with them as a nursemaid. During this time Bakhita was introduced to the Catholic faith through the Canossian Sisters of Charity. She said, "I enjoyed the opportunity to be instructed in the Christian faith. The saintly sisters helped me to know God, whom I had experienced in my heart since childhood." Bakhita asked to stay at the convent, and she was permitted to do so.

On January 9, 1890, Bakhita was baptized in the Catholic Church and experienced "such joy that only angels could describe!" She took the name Giuseppina (Josephine). Before long, Josephine discerned a vocation, and six years later she took the habit of the Canossian Sisters of Charity. She spent her days in humble service, working in the kitchen and doing embroidery and sewing. When her biography was published in 1930, Sister Josephine was asked to speak in public settings. She used these opportunities to further the cause of the missions.

Of the difficult days of slavery and those who mistreated her, Sister Josephine said, "If I were to meet the slave-traders who kidnapped me and even those who tortured me, I would kneel and kiss their hands, for if that did not happen, I would not be a Christian and religious today." Sister Josephine Bakhita, affectionately called "Mother Moretta" (Black Mother) died on February 8, 1947 and was canonized on October 1, 2000 by Pope John Paul II. Indeed, Bakhita had become "the Fortunate One."

FAITH IN ACTION

Romans 8:28 says, "We know that in everything God works for good with those who love him, who are called according to his purpose." God worked great good out of Sister Josephine Bakhita's suffering. What painful experience has God used in my life to work great good for me or for another? Can you thank Him for that experience?

Lesson One

Healing for the Wounded Heart

Prayer for Hidden Grief

Oh, the untold secret grief
that draws back from all relief,
will not deign to have a cure,
Grieves and says: I must endure.

Ah, the tear — soon wiped away —
wipes in haste with no delay,
lest some sympathizing eye
might the weeping sad espy.

Ah, the heart's great heaving groan,
quickly silenced lest the moan
might attack some friendly heart
and, to save, at once to start.

God of mercy, known alone
to Thee is the saddening groan,
to Thee is the falling tear,
God of mercy, hear, oh hear.

BENJAMIN TUCKER TANNER

WEEKLY THEME

God wants to heal the wounds of my heart. Women of Grace can receive true healing by embracing the graces available to us in the life of the resurrected Christ.

WEEKLY GRACE

I pray for the grace to see the wounds of my heart and to surrender them to the healing love of God.

Full of Grace: Read pages 167 - 170 in the text, and then answer the following questions.

1. Healing wounds of the heart is sometimes called "inner healing" or "healing of memories." Why do you think such healing is important if we are to fulfill our mission as women of grace?

2. Specifically, how do we cooperate with the grace of God for healing to take place?

3. Read the *Catechism of the Catholic Church,* No. 1735. To what extent might this apply to Tina (pages 169 –170)?

4. Authentic spirituality requires a willingness to address those hurtful episodes in our lives that may be stunting our spiritual growth. Sometimes old issues resurface, causing us to make poor decisions today. Do I have unresolved relationships, or unresolved, dangerous, or sinful habits? Am I willing to let God heal them? Why or why not?

KNOW THE FAITH

God the Father Almighty

One of God's attributes is His omnipotence: He is all-powerful and, therefore, can do all things. The angel Gabriel speaks to this when he tells the Virgin Mary that Elizabeth has conceived a child in her old age, for "nothing is impossible with God" (Luke 1:36). Our Lady attests to this fact as well in her Magnificat: "God who is mighty has done great things for me" (Luke 1:49).

Scripture is filled with the omnipotent action of God. From the first chapter of Genesis, to the parting of the Red Sea, to Christ's Resurrection from the dead, we see the incomparable might of the Most High God. We need to remember this omnipotence when we ask God for healing. When we surrender our pain and suffering to God's holy will, there is no wound too great, too deep, or too difficult for Him to heal.

Read paragraphs 268 –274 in the *Catechism of the Catholic Church,* and then answer the following questions.

1. Paragraph 268 gives three qualities of God's power. What are they, and how do they increase your faith in God's desire and capacity to heal the wounds of your heart?

2. In what two ways does God show His "fatherly" omnipotence (No. 270)? Consider how God's "wise intellect" (No. 271), also known as His omniscience (all-knowing) may influence the length of our healing process as well as the kind of healing we receive? (For example, the patience and perseverance we learn by accepting a difficulty rather than removing it altogether.)

3. Read again Paragraphs 272 – 274. How do our weaknesses, exemplified by the woundedness of our hearts, draw us to the power of Christ ?

WORD TO KNOW

Sin: "...an offense against reason, truth, and right conscience" caused by an inordinate attachment to certain goods. All sin wounds the nature of man and injures human solidarity (see CCC, No. 1849). The gravity of sin is distinguished by mortal sin (deadly) and venial sin (wounding but not fatal to the soul). Mortal sin must concern *grave matter* that is committed with *full knowledge* and with *deliberate and free consent*. There is no sin that cannot be forgiven (see Matthew 16:19).

FOR PONDERING...

Inner Peace

In my years of teaching Bible classes in various parishes, women have come to me privately looking for help — women who have had abortions, been involved in sexual sin, women who have been abused sexually. I have learned that when a friend opens her heart to you and confesses something out of her past, you are being put to the test.

Your friend has chosen to confide in you because she sees Jesus in you. She has experienced shame and rejection; she may be struggling to believe that her sins can be forgiven. She is looking for reassurance from you. You will have only a second to react. If you look shocked, draw back, or show revulsion, the woman may decide her sin is so terrible that she can never be accepted by other women.

In the moment your friend opens her heart to you, you are called to be a sign of God's absolute forgiving love. Ask God to fill you with His love for this His daughter, and to let that love shine through your eyes. Assure your friend that God loves her and that there is nothing she has done that God can't forgive. If it is appropriate, comfort your friend as a mother comforts her child.

Gently ask if she has been to confession, and if not encourage her to go. Offer to go with her. I usually suggest a priest who is particularly sensitive in such matters. I will either go in first and tell him what is coming or call ahead and set up an appointment. A woman who has not confessed serious sin is often afraid that the priest will be shocked by what she says or will reject her altogether. Knowing that the priest already knows the "big" thing and is expecting her, gives her the courage to speak. In some cases, the priest may explain to the woman that, in spite of the guilt she feels, given her age or the circumstances, she didn't commit a mortal sin.

I cannot describe the joy I feel when I see a friend who has been set free emerging from the confessional, her face radiant with joy.

DO'L

Read 2 Corinthians 1: 3-7. How do the healed wounds of our hearts prepare us to be a source of healing and God's mercy in the lives of others?

____

____

____

____

IN CLOSING...

"My child, all your sins have not wounded My Heart as painfully as your present lack of trust does — that after so many efforts of My love and mercy, you should still doubt my goodness...Tell me all, My child, hide nothing from Me, because My loving Heart, the Heart of your Best Friend, is listening to you."

OUR LORD TO ST. FAUSTINA KOWALSKA

Dear Lord,
How often presumption convinces me that You do not want to heal me or that my sin is too great for You! Heal me of this infirmity of spirit. Give me trust, faith, and confidence in You. Help me to surrender to Your fatherly love and concern, and to know the intimacy of Your healing presence.
Amen.

Lesson Two

Identifying Wounds of the Heart

Prayer: Anima Christi (*"Soul of Christ"*)

Soul of Christ, sanctify me.
Body of Christ, heal me.
Blood of Christ, fill me.
Water from the side of Christ, wash me.
Passion of Christ, strengthen me.
O Good Jesus, hear me.

Within your wounds, hide me.
Never permit me to be separated from Thee.
From the wicked enemy, defend me.
At the hour of my death, call me and
bid me come unto Thee,
that with Thy saints I may praise Thee
forever and ever. Amen.

WEEKLY THEME

God wants to heal the wounds of my heart. Women of Grace can receive true healing by embracing the graces available to us in the life of the resurrected Christ.

WEEKLY GRACE

I pray for the grace to see the wounds of my heart and to surrender them to the healing love of God.

Full of Grace: Read pages 170 - 176 in the text, and then answer the following questions.

1. What are the five questions that help us to identify wounds of the heart?

a. ______________________________

b. ______________________________

c. ______________________________

d. ______________________________

e. ______________________________

Do any of these questions apply to you? If so, which ones? For what might you need inner healing?

____

____

____

____

2. How can we begin to get to the root cause of a problem? Why is it important to do so?

3. List some of the insights Tina gained through the prayer for inner healing. Which one speaks most to you, and why?

4. Read Psalm 139. Which verses do you think relate to the area of inner healing? Which verses touch you most deeply, and why?

KNOW THE FAITH

The Gift of Emotions

A sudden rush of joy at the beauty of a sunset. A stab of pain at the memory of a deceased loved one. The flood of love at a baby's smile. The rising heat of sudden anger. The smoldering ember of sustained hatred. The flash of fear at perceived danger. All of these phrases describe a fundamental function of the human person — an emotional response.

An emotion is a psychological reaction to stimuli from the world around us or from thoughts, memories, and our imagination that we sense through our bodily feelings. The *Catechism of the Catholic Church* calls the emotions "passions," and tells us they are the part of the human psyche that form the passageway between the life of the senses and the life of the mind (No. 1764). The healthy functioning of our emotions is necessary for psychological wholeness and health.

Along with his colleagues, Dr. Conrad Baars, a psychiatrist noted for his work in integrating a Catholic understanding of the human person with contemporary psychology, calls the emotions *psychic motors* because they move a person to feel about something in the interior of his being, or they move him towards action. These two functions of the emotions group them into two categories — the *humane emotions* (also called the *emotions of the pleasure appetite* and the *utilitarian emotions* (also called the *assertive emotions*).

The humane emotions cause an inner movement in the human person. When these emotions have been allowed to function as they were designed by God to do, these emotions are aroused by everything that is good, loveable, and pleasurable, and also by that which opposes the good, loveable, and pleasurable. The six humane emotions are love or liking, desire, joy, hate or dislike, aversion, and sadness. According to Dr. Baars, they make up the "heart" or inner core of man's emotional life. Likewise, the *Catechism* recalls that Our Lord referred to man's heart as the source from which his passions spring (cf. Mark 7:21).

The next group of emotions gives us the energy to move into action. They are called the *utilitarian* or *assertive* emotions. The first two are hope (including confidence, trust, expectation, optimism) and despair (including hopelessness and pessimism), and they operate to move us toward a goal or away from it. The rest of the emotions in this group function to help us respond to whatever is harmful to our life, safety, freedom, or general well being. They are courage (including boldness, fearlessness, fortitude, etc.) and fear (dread, timidity, anxiety, fright, panic). The last assertive or utilitarian emotion is anger, often called the "ultimate emotion" because it rouses to protect us from almost certain harm or injustice. Like many of the other emotions, anger has a full range of intensities such as irritation, annoyance, wrath, and rage.

The emotions are necessary for normal, healthy living. Therefore, there are no negative or bad emotions (see CCC, No. 1767). There are only negative or bad responses to our emotions. Our emotions must be subject to our reason and our will, and our reason and our will must be formed in light of Sacred Scripture and the teachings of the Catholic Church. In this way, our emotions achieve their full purpose in helping us attain emotional maturity and in aiding us on our path to holiness.

An example illustrates the point. Imagine you are about to be fired over something you did not do. Anger surges through you at this injustice, but how should you respond? Act out of that anger, dash into the boss's office, and create a scene (or worse)? Or, allow the first rush of anger to subside, collect your thoughts, and make an appointment with the supervisor, to try to straighten the matter out? In the first instance, anger rules our reason and our will. In the second, reason and will rule our anger. In the first instance, we sin against charity. In the second, we act with courtesy and filial respect. As the *Catechism* tells us, "Emotions and feelings can be taken up into the *virtues* or perverted by the *vices*" (No. 1770).

The human person develops a healthy emotional life when the full measure (or range) of his emotional reactions are "tamed." This occurs as one exercises both the gift of reason and of free will, which have been shaped by the love of God and neighbor. It is when the emotions are denied or repressed that emotional difficulties ensue and inner healing is necessary. Attempts to interfere with the natural functioning of emotions will have adverse effects and lead to much heartache and pain.

1. Many people think that emotions and feelings are the same. While all emotions are feelings, not all feelings are emotions. Can you think of some feelings that are not emotions?

____

____

____

____

2. How do the humane emotions make us more human when they are fully integrated with our reason and our will? How do they help us become a conduit of grace in the world?

____

____

____

____

3. Some people were taught as children to hide their emotions or to repress them. Why do you think this leads to emotional struggles later?

____

____

____

WORD TO KNOW

Emotion: From the Latin *ex-motus,* having to do with motion or movement. This may refer to reactions to the world around us or within our own inner psychic world.

FOR PONDERING…

Smile, God Loves You — And He's With You!

Twenty-eight years ago, I gave my life to Christ. This was long before I had any idea about His Church. I didn't feel anything at the time; there was no experience that I was aware of. But I decided to trust that if He was God, He knew how to be God … I would wait. The next morning when I opened my eyes, I said for the first time in my life, "Good morning, Lord." I knew that He is God, and that I'd never be alone again. The emptiness and pain I had lived with was gone. I was overwhelmed by His love.

Have you ever felt that, while you might sometimes make a good impression upon people, if they really knew you, they wouldn't be so impressed? Well, here was Someone — God — Who knew me better than anyone else could know me. If anyone had a reason to not like me, it was God. And yet, I knew that morning that He who knew me best, loved me most. Psalm 139 became my favorite psalm:

Thou searchest out my path and my lying down,
and art acquainted with all my ways.
Even before a word is on my tongue…
O LORD, thou knowest it altogether.

PSALMS 139:3-4

The Holy Spirit — our tender, indwelling Guide and Stay — spoke words through the prophet Isaiah that are also for us!

Fear not, for I am with you,
be not dismayed, for I am your God;
I will strengthen you, I will help you,
I will uphold you with my victorious right hand.

ISAIAH 41:10

Some would say, "I don't *feel* strengthened. I'm *not* healed. I want to honor God. I want to believe. But the hurts I've experienced are too deep. I'm not able to get past them."

Let me say first that you're not alone. We are victims of a fallen world. Most of us have at one time or other been visited by death or loss or loneliness or abuse of some kind. So how can we experience the abundant life that our Lord came from heaven to give us? Here are a few suggestions:

- *Pray.* When we don't feel like praying, that's the time we need to pray the most. Don't allow the enemy to get a foothold. In fact, you might even begin with a novena to the Holy Spirit.
- *Find a prayer partner.* Ask the Holy Spirit to direct you to a friend with whom you can pray. Prayer partners pray with and for each other, encourage each other, and keep one other accountable.
- *Attend daily Mass* as often as possible. Try to make at least one Holy Hour before the Blessed Sacrament each week.
- *Forgive.* That's the hardest one. Even so, you must. Why? Because those who have hurt you deserve your forgiveness? No. But neither do we deserve God's forgiveness. When all else fails, the only way is to "Forgive as God in Christ has forgiven you."
- *Love your Mother.* Draw near to the spouse of the Holy Spirit, the Blessed Virgin Mary. She will teach you how to pray, how to forgive, how to offer your sufferings to God, how to draw near to Him with a love that is beyond all you have ever known.

RM

Read Isaiah 49:14-16. What does the Lord tell us in this passage? How can Rosalind's suggestions help us to recall these words when we most need to remember them?

____

____

____

IN CLOSING...

"Why should a word, which would at other times remain on the surface of our soul, sometimes sink to a great depth and inflict a cruel wound? Perhaps in such moments our soul is already bruised by other sufferings and ready to overflow, and thus finds itself nearer to the exterior, closer to painful blows and brutal incomprehension."

ELISABETH LESEUR

Dear Lord,

I am often hurt deeply over what some would call trifles and aggravations. Perhaps my reaction is caused by some deep-seated wound that has not yet healed. In the light of Your Spirit, reveal to me that which has been hidden in darkness. Help me to enter into the mystery of Your redemptive grace. Give me courage to seek the healing I need, and perseverance to stay the course. In Jesus' name I pray. Amen.

Lesson Three

Obstacles to Inner Healing

Prayer: The *Confiteor*

I confess to almighty God
and to you, my brothers and sisters,
that I have sinned through my own fault,
in my thoughts and in my words,
in what I have done
and in what I have failed to do;
and I ask blessed Mary, ever virgin,
all the angels and saints,
and you, my brothers and sisters,
to pray for me to the Lord our God.

WEEKLY THEME

God wants to heal the wounds of my heart. Women of Grace can receive true healing by embracing the graces available to us in the life of the resurrected Christ.

WEEKLY GRACE

I pray for the grace to see the wounds of my heart and to surrender them to the healing love of God.

Full of Grace: Read pages 176 - 180 in the text, and then answer the following questions.

1. What are five obstacles to inner healing? Which might be obstacles for you?

   a. ______________________________

   b. ______________________________

   c. ______________________________

   d. ______________________________

   e. ______________________________

2. Have you erected a "wall of resistance" to God's healing love? If so, how? What can you do to tear it down?

   ____

   ____

   ____

3. Have you sabotaged your own healing process? How, and what practical strategy can you put in place to be victorious?

   ____

   ____

   ____

4. Inner healing involves sacrifice. Ask God to show you what you must do to experience the healing you seek. Write down what sacrifice you sense He is asking of you.

____

____

____

KNOW THE FAITH

Emotional Disorders and Trauma

Some people grow to chronological adulthood stunted in their emotional maturity, and many others have discovered less severe, but nonetheless real, areas within them that need the gentle touch of the Holy Spirit to bring them inner healing and wholeness.

As we have discovered, the healthy functioning of our emotions is necessary for a psychologically healthy and productive life. It is also necessary for our spiritual growth and development. When our emotions do not function as they should, emotional struggles, problems, or disorders occur.

Several factors can cause our emotional health to become impaired to a greater or lesser degree. For example, every human person has an innate need and desire to be loved for who he or she is. In the revised edition of his book, *Feeling and Healing Your Emotions,* Dr. Baars writes, "When a child is deprived in infancy, childhood, or puberty of the most fundamental element of emotional nourishment, namely, the unselfish, mature love of an adult person, he remains incapable of experiencing joy and happiness."

This deprivation leads the child to crave that which he does not experience, and to the extent that his desire is frustrated, his humane emotions cannot develop. On the other hand, his assertive emotions develop to an excessive level. These could be manifested in fear, despair, or too much energetic striving. Though he grows and develops physically, to a greater or lesser degree emotionally he remains a child and no amount of success makes him feel adequate, capable or suited for adult life. When a serious crisis comes, this individual is likely to cave in, his facade cracking in the heat of pressure. The lynch pins of his seemingly well-ordered life prove to be no more than sawdust blown away by the winds of the storm. He comes undone. This disorder, known as emotional deprivation disorder, leads to many other kinds of emotional difficulties and, left untreated, can progress to serious depression and even suicide.

Yet another way in which emotional health is impaired comes from false or erroneous ideas imparted to the child about his feelings or emotions, causing him to experience shame or guilt about them. This misunderstanding stimulates two of the assertive emotions, fear and/or energy (hope or courage), which repress the original emotion. Rather than making that emotion go away, however, it becomes "buried alive," only to rise up later in some detrimental way — possibly through passive/aggressive behaviors, an obsessive compulsive disorder, phobias, scrupulosity, or an hysterical neurosis.

Even when these emotional difficulties do not progress to a full-blown disorder, they can impede our interactions with God and with others. Often an unhealthy independence or an unhealthy dependence develops toward others that tests and tries the most loving of relationships. Emotional distance or a smothering need can manifest itself. God may well become the "ogre parent" who never gave the necessary love, or the "taskmaster parent" whose affection we must win through performance or achievement. An unhealthy fear of authority, or an inordinate desire to please, or a driving need to be constantly involved in projects or general busy-ness can ensue. An attempt to escape the pain through drug or alcohol consumption only exacerbates the problem adding yet another layer to spiritual, emotional, and relational difficulties.

Emotions can also be marred by a variety of experiences and traumas, including all forms of abuse (physical, sexual, verbal), the early loss of a parent, witnessing a heinous crime, abandonment issues as a result of divorce or other circumstances, a sense of failure, and mistreatment at the hands of peers to name a few.

This could lead us all to despair, if not for the love and mercy of God Who tells us that He will restore what the locusts have eaten (Joel 3:25), and that He will give us a new heart (Ezekiel 11:19-20). To accomplish His purposes, He provides us with the sacraments, with prayer, with priests and spiritual directors, and with Catholic physicians and mental health counselors who can help us along the path to wholeness and health. God desires that we experience the fullness of life that He intends for us. He desires to restore us, to renew us, and to set us free. And, in so doing, we become a conduit of His love in the world.

1. What is emotional deprivation disorder and what causes it? How can this be detrimental to our spiritual growth?

____

____

____

2. Some of us remember being told that certain emotions and feelings were "unladylike," "inappropriate," or just plain "bad." What were they? How did you respond?

____

____

____

3. Read Joel 3: 25 and Ezekiel 11: 19-20. If we believe that God is an almighty God, do we believe that He can do what He says in these passages? Do you believe He can and will do this for you?

____

____

____

WORD TO KNOW

Affirmation: In psychological terms, communicating to another human person through attentive, affective presence his intrinsic goodness, worth, and "loveableness." Through being present, allowing oneself to feel for the other, and revealing one's affection in one's countenance, tone of voice or touch, affirmation proclaims the value of the human person for who he is, not for what he does or accomplishes. Affirmation is primarily *affective* rather than *effective* — meaning that even praising the other, while a positive and important thing to do, is not affirmation itself. Affirmation is essential for the healthy growth and development of the emotions.

FOR PONDERING…

Hidden Anger

Repressed anger is a major obstacle to inner healing. Christian women know they should forgive, and yet some confuse this with the false notion that they should never get angry.

Some grew up in homes where their parents punished them for being angry. When this happened, these parents failed to help their children to distinguish between appropriate feelings of anger and inappropriate ways to respond to it. This leaves the child confused and with the erroneous belief that her feelings are wrong.

When we see evil or injustice, the normal healthy reaction is anger. God gets angry. Jesus got angry (cf. Mt 15:1-14, 21:12-13, 23:23-29). Yet, Jesus did not sin in His dealings with the moneychangers in the temple, or with the scribes and Pharisees. As the Scripture reminds us, "Be angry, but do not sin" (Eph 4:25-27).

If you shove your angry feelings down — bury them alive — they will rise up to haunt you. You may engage in what those in the mental health field call passive/aggressive behaviors. Rather than showing your anger openly, you covertly sabotage activities and relationships. Since forgiveness is often at the heart of inner healing, a necessary step is to learn to recognize your feelings of anger.

Josie came to talk to me about her guilt. She felt she was a terrible person because she didn't want to go and see her mother. She had confessed her sin and still felt guilty. As we talked, Josie revealed numerous ways in which her mother had been cruel, abusive, intrusive, and manipulative. Her mother's behavior was totally unacceptable, but Josie kept blaming herself and excusing her mother.

I explained to Josie how she was skipping over the first step of the forgiving process. I told her, "You can't forgive until you have acknowledged how you have been hurt. You have to feel the anger you have been repressing — anger that is manifesting itself as guilt feelings. Once you do that, you will be able to really forgive. What you are doing now is excusing, and that isn't healthy."

It took Josie some time to be comfortable with expressing her anger, but when she did she was able to sincerely forgive and her guilt feelings disappeared. She was also able to recognize when love obliged her not to accept her mother's misbehavior. In time, their relationship improved.

DO'L

Have I buried any feelings or emotions that may manifest themselves in unacceptable ways?

____

____

IN CLOSING…

"When blood no longer flows from an open wound, to the indifferent eye it seems that healing is near. Nothing could be more wrong; the wound that no longer bleeds is one that will never heal."

ELISABETH LESEUR

Dear Lord,

Many wounds are hidden within the depths of my heart, wounds that even I do not know exist. Yet these wounds separate me from You and from others. Through the light of Your Holy Spirit, illuminate those wounds that "no longer bleed" so that Your healing power might enter in and restore me to the fullness of life. Give me the grace to forgive and to seek forgiveness, to be reconciled and to seek reconciliation, to hope and to be a source of hope to others. Amen.

Lesson Four

Lack of Forgiveness: The Greatest Obstacle of All

Prayer Before the Crucifix

Look down upon me, good and gentle Jesus,
while before Your face I humbly kneel.
With burning affection,
I pray, fix deep in my heart
lively sentiments of
faith, hope and love,
true contrition for my sins
and a firm purpose of amendment.
Amen.

WEEKLY THEME
God wants to heal the wounds of my heart. Women of Grace can receive true healing by embracing the graces available to us in the life of the resurrected Christ.

WEEKLY GRACE
I pray for the grace to see the wounds of my heart and to surrender them to the healing love of God.

Full of Grace: Read pages 180 – 187 in the text, and then answer the following questions.

1. Why is lack of forgiveness the greatest obstacle to inner healing?

2. Which of the Scripture quotes on pages 180 – 187 speak to you the most? Why?

3. What are some of the misconceptions about what forgiveness means?

4. What steps can we take to encourage our healing process of forgiveness?

KNOW THE FAITH

Forgiveness — The Path to Peace

The following is an excerpt from the Lenten Message given by Pope John Paul II in 2001 (paragraph 4).

> *The only path to peace is forgiveness. Forgiveness given and received enables a new kind of relationship among people, breaking the spiral of hatred and revenge and shattering the chains of evil which bind the hearts of those in conflict with one another.*
>
> *This is a challenge not only to individuals but also to communities, peoples, and humanity as a whole. In a special way it concerns families. It is not easy to be converted to forgiveness and reconciliation. To choose reconciliation can seem problematic enough when we ourselves are at fault. But if the fault is someone else's, reconciliation may even seem a senseless humiliation. An inner conversion is required if this step is to be taken; the courage to be humbly obedient to Jesus' command is needed. His word leaves no doubt: not only those who provoke hostility but also those who are its victims must seek reconciliation (cf. Mt. 5:23-24).*
>
> *Christians must make peace even when they feel that they are victims of those who have struck and hurt them unjustly. This was how the Lord himself acted. He expects his disciples to follow him, and in this way cooperate in redeeming his brothers and sisters.*
>
> *In our own time, forgiveness appears more and more essential if there is to be genuine social renewal and a consolidation of peace in the world. In proclaiming forgiveness and love of enemies, the Church is aware of adding to the spiritual heritage of all humanity a new mode of human relationships; an arduous mode, to be sure, but one that is also rich in hope. In this, the Church knows she can rely on the help of the Lord, who never abandons those who turn to him in times of difficulty.*

1. Why do you think the Holy Father says that forgiveness is the only path to peace? How does it create a "new kind of relationship among people?"

2. Who must seek reconciliation and why is an inner conversion necessary to do it?

3. Read the *Catechism of the Catholic Church*, No. 2303. What does it say about deliberate hatred? Is this something about which you personally need to be concerned? How can you effectively work toward ameliorating it?

WORD TO KNOW

Forgive: In the New Testament, two Greek words are translated as "forgive." They represent the two sides of forgiveness. *Aphiemi* means to send away, to cancel completely a debt. *Charizomai*, Greek for "grace," means to extend an unmerited gift.

FOR PONDERING...

Write It Off

When I am talking about forgiveness, people will often ask: "Why do I have to go back into my past and forgive things that happened years ago?"

When we are hurt and angry, we can decide either to forgive or to hold on to resentment. If we choose not to forgive, that decision remains in force. If you say, "I won't forgive," your unforgiveness continues very much into the present.

Jesus couldn't have been more explicit about our obligation to forgive. "If you do not forgive men their sins, your heavenly Father will not forgive your sins" (Mt 6:15).

A woman came up to me after a talk on forgiveness and told me that she would never forgive those who had hurt her. I said, "Well, then, you should not say the Our Father because you are asking God not to forgive you."

She replied, "Oh, I don't say that part."

The tragedy of this attitude is that when we don't forgive old injuries, we are only hurting ourselves. The people who hurt us may have forgotten what they did. They may have gone to confession and been forgiven. They may have died and been judged. They could be in heaven, but if we don't forgive we are trapped in resentment. We go on experiencing the old hurt.

However, Jesus offers us an easy way out: forgive. You don't have to feel forgiving. It isn't about feelings — it is about an act of the will. Think of it as writing off an old debt, one the person who owed you wasn't going to pay anyway.

If you agree to stop demanding payment on the debt, an amazing thing happens — Jesus Himself takes care of the debt. He heals the wound. As long as you are holding on and demanding payment from the person who hurt you, you are preventing Jesus from healing the wound.

When you think about it, forgiveness in Christ is a very good deal. We would be foolish not to accept His forgiveness for all our sins in exchange for our forgiving debts that weren't going to be paid anyway. We have everything to gain and nothing to lose — except a lot of emotional pain and suffering.

DO'L

Is there someone from whom I should stop "demanding payment?" Who and for what? What step am I willing to take to do so?

IN CLOSING...

"When you are tormented by any passion or evil inclination, if you be so weak as to yield to it, and let it lead you, take it for a certain truth, that it will take deeper root, wage a more violent war against you. But if you resist it courageously at first, it will daily diminish. Every day it will have less strength to act upon you, till at length, it will come to have none at all."

ST. DOROTHEUS

Dear Lord,
Give me the grace to forgive as soon as I am wronged or mistreated, so that no evil inclination can take root in me. With Your help, I seek to let go of old grudges, resist the temptation to dwell on past injuries, and relinquish all bitterness and resentment. Let Your mercy take up residence in me so that I may extend it to others. I pray this in the Name of Christ our Lord. Amen.

Lesson Five

Two Stories of the Power of Forgiveness

Prayer of St. Francis

Lord, make me an instrument of Thy peace,
where there is hatred, let me sow your love;
where there is injury, pardon;
where there is doubt, faith;
where there is despair, hope;
where there is darkness, light;
and where there is sadness joy.

O Divine Master, grant that I may not so much
seek to be consoled as to console;
to be understood as to understand;
to be loved, as to love;
for it is in giving that we receive,
it is in pardoning that we are pardoned,
and it is in dying that we are born to eternal life.
Amen.

WEEKLY THEME
God wants to heal the wounds of my heart. Women of Grace can receive true healing by embracing the graces available to us in the life of the resurrected Christ.

WEEKLY GRACE
I pray for the grace to see the wounds of my heart and to surrender them to the healing love of God.

Full of Grace: Read pages 187 – 193 in the text, then answer the following questions.

1. In what way are humans "triune" beings, and what does this triune nature tell us about sickness and healing?

2. Read the *Catechism of the Catholic Church*, No. 2840. Why can we not experience God's mercy if we have not forgiven others?

3. Read the *Catechism of the Catholic Church*, No. 2843. Where is everything "bound and loosed," and what does the heart do with injury and hurt when it is surrendered to the Holy Spirit?

____

____

____

4. Recall the stories of Bill and Audrey. How were their healings a "resurrection from the dead?" How have you been encouraged to let the resurrection power of Jesus Christ affect you?

____

____

____

KNOW THE FAITH

Seeking Forgiveness

Jesus said, "So if you are offering your gift at the altar, and there remember that your brother has something against you, leave your gift there before the altar and go; be reconciled to your brother, and then come and offer your gift" (Mt 5:23-24).

This passage communicates an important truth — not only must we forgive, we must also ask to be forgiven. The reality is, just as others have sinned against us, so too have we sinned against others. And, just as lack of forgiveness holds us in bondage to a past event, so too are we held bound by a failure to seek forgiveness from others.

Asking for forgiveness is often not easy. Four reasons loom large: pride, disregard for our neighbor, poor self-observation, and stubbornness. In place of these, we must pray for the virtues of humility, charity, self-knowledge, and docility.

Pride takes many forms: self-justification, defensiveness, and an arrogance that prevents us from admitting a wrong. Humility, on the other hand, acknowledges the truth of our condition — we are imperfect creatures in serious need of a Savior.

Disregard for our neighbor finds its outlet in insensitivity, apathetic disinterest, or contempt. Charity, on the other hand, gives us the lens to see our neighbor as "another self" who is made in the image and likeness of God.

Poor self-observation may well be the greatest difficulty in failing to ask for forgiveness; we simply do not see how our attitudes, actions, and words affect others. We must beg God for the gift of self-knowledge. This will help us to recognize the relationship between the wounds of our heart and our motivations and behaviors.

Finally, the iron fist of stubbornness often clenches even our best intentions in its unrelenting grasp. The antidote to stubbornness is the virtue of docility, which makes us flexible in the hand of God and ready to move with the breath of His Holy Spirit.

No matter what the spiritual or emotional malady might be, however, there is no real excuse for *not* asking for forgiveness; doing so is intimately tied to making ourselves an acceptable gift at the altar of the Lord. When we acknowledge our sin and confess it to God in the Sacrament of Penance, we open ourselves to receive the grace we need to approach the one we have injured, to seek his pardon. How many families, friendships, and professional relationships have been restored through a simple request for forgiveness? How many destroyed for lack of this simple act?

Asking for forgiveness, however, is only a beginning. Saying, "I'm sorry" without making an on-going effort to change our behavior is unacceptable. Our sincerity is proven one deed at a time. Finally, we must make restitution. True contrition compels us to make up for the "loss" we have caused. We must work to repair the damage caused by our loose tongue, impetuous actions, or rash judgments. In all cases, we must pray for the party we have offended, asking God to salve the wounds we have inflicted and bring our neighbor to complete and total healing in Him.

1. Of the four reasons given for why we don't seek forgiveness from others, which one are you most susceptible to? What is its antidote? In what way can you practice this virtue now so you can ask to be forgiven as soon as you give offense?

2. Can you recall a time when a sincere apology mended a relationship? Tell about it here.

3. Read the *Catechism of the Catholic Church*, No. 1459. What does it say about making satisfaction for our sins against others? How does this work for our good as well as the good of our neighbor?

WORD TO KNOW

Suffer: From the Greek *pascho*, from which the word "passion" comes, as in the Passion of our Lord Jesus Christ. The reality of a suffering God is an impenetrable mystery. Similarly, the value and meaning of our own suffering is hard to comprehend. It is essential, however, to join together these two realities (the suffering of God and that of our own) in order for them to bear supernatural fruit.

FOR PONDERING...

After Forgiveness

Forgiveness of past injuries can be the emotional equivalent of major surgery. When we open our memories to the healing power of the Holy Spirit, God comes in like a skillful surgeon and removes the obstruction to our spiritual growth.

The Scripture says, "He that hates his brother is in darkness, and walks in darkness, and knows not where he is going, because that darkness has blinded his eyes" (1 Jn 2:11).

A personal story illustrates how blind we can become when hatred fills our heart, and obstructs our spiritual growth. A friend of mine suffers from a learning disability, and is unable to read. Unfortunately, when she was in school, her teachers and her mother did not understand her problem and thought she was not trying to learn. The frustration of both mother and daughter drove a wedge between them, irreparably harming their relationship.

One day, my friend saw a matchbook cover with an advertisement for art school. It showed a picture and said, "Draw this." She made a perfect copy of the illustration and showed it to her mother. Instead of receiving encouragement, my friend was rebuffed. Her mother tore up her picture and told her she had no artistic talent. Because of this and many similar incidents, hatred toward her mother grew in my friend's heart. This hatred caused a psychological blindness. Though her eyes functioned perfectly, she simply could not "see" the disarray of her home. Others could, however, including her family, who begged and pleaded with her to do something about it, all to no avail. My friend simply would not do anything to improve the appearance of her home, insisting all the while that the frayed carpet and stained wallpaper were perfectly fine.

After much struggle, my friend decided to forgive her mother for all of the wounds of the heart she had inflicted upon her. She followed through, forgave her mother, and experienced Jesus' loving forgiveness. When my friend went home, she was shocked! She seemed to see her house for the first time as it really was, and she was appalled! Immediately the wallpaper was ripped down and the carpet was removed. Her family was overjoyed! With the cataracts of unforgiveness removed from her eyes, she could see clearly — spiritually and psychologically.

From time to time we are all poor self-observers. Is there an area of my life about which family members complain even though I see no problem? Could my "blindness" suggest a need for inner healing or a forgiving heart? Do I need to ask my family for their forgiveness?

____

____

____

IN CLOSING...

"You ask me for a method of attaining perfection. I know of love — and only love. Love can do all things."

ST. THERESE OF LISIEUX

Dear Lord,
My own ability to love is so weak and impoverished. But, Your love in me can do all things. Fill me with Your love, that I might forgive. Fill me with Your love, that I might ask for forgiveness from others. Make me a channel of Your peace, today and always. Amen.

Chapter Eight

Carrying Out the Mission: Embracing the Abundant Life

Full of Grace: This week covers pages 195-227 of the text.

In this our final week of the foundational *Women of Grace*® study, we will conclude by taking all we have learned in the preceding weeks and exploring how those gifts empower us to fulfill God's perfect plan for each of us. That plan, as we have said already, is to bring the love of Christ to the world, just as Mary did, and like her to be spiritual mothers to those the Lord entrusts to our care.

Jesus said, "Go into all the nations and make them my disciples…believers will be given the power to perform miracles." Imagine what the apostles must have felt when they heard His words! The thrill! The responsibility!

We are to share in that responsibility, just as men and women of every generation who have embraced Jesus' command and promise. Some were numbered among the learned or powerful; most were ordinary people who believed that, through them, Christ would do great things. Boot-makers, bakers, weavers, wives… down through the centuries, receptive souls have taken His call to heart.

LESSON ONE — Heralds of the Gospel
LESSON TWO — Mary Brings the Word of God to the World
LESSON THREE — Mary Intercedes for God's Children
LESSON FOUR — Mary Suffers, Too
LESSON FIVE — The Hour Has Come: How Will We Respond?

Questions To Ponder This Week

- What graces do I need most in order to imitate my heavenly Mother?
- Each era of human history calls forth saints to spread the Good News of the Gospel. What "saints in the making" have I encountered in my own lifetime?

Media Response Sheet

Carrying Out the Mission: Embracing the Abundant Life

Answer the following questions as you watch the pre-recorded lesson given by Johnnette S. Benkovic, founder of Women of Grace®.

WEEKLY THEME
Fully surrendered as Women of Grace and following in the footsteps of the Blessed Virgin Mary, we are called to "aid humanity in not falling."

WEEKLY GRACE
I pray for the grace to accept my mission as a Woman of Grace and to pattern my life after the Blessed Virgin Mary.

1. Through whom do we learn to be Christ-bearers who bring Jesus Christ to the world?

   ____

   ____

2. Prayer invoking Mary's intercession dates back to the ______________ century. This prayer is called the ______________ ______________.

3. A mediator serves as a vehicle for bringing about ______________ and ______________ between ______________.

4. Who is the one mediator between God and man?

   ____

   ____

5. What sacrament gives us a share in Jesus' ministry of mediation?

   ____

   ____

6. Jesus is the first mediator; we are called ______________ ______________.

7. In what three ways does Mary mediate as a spiritual mother?

   a. ______________________________

   b. ______________________________

   c. ______________________________

8. How did Mary bring the Word of God to the world, and how do we do the same?

____

9. What three excuses are often given for not evangelizing?

a. _______________

b. _______________

c. _______________

10. What is perhaps the most effective way to evangelize?

____

____

11. What three parts of our story make up our testimony?

a. _______________

b. _______________

c. _______________

12. How do we share our faith without being offensive?

____

____

13. What are the five key actions of an effective intercessor?

a. _______________

b. _______________

c. _______________

d. _______________

e. _______________

14. What is perhaps the keenest way in which Mary intercedes?

____

15. As Women of Grace, what are we called to do with our difficulties?

____

16. Where is God leading us?

____

____

Woman of Grace

St. Frances Cabrini (1850-1917)

Through prayer we discover God's perfect plan for our lives. Prayer is also how we find the courage to embark upon that plan, and the perseverance to bring it to completion. Such was the case with Mary Francesca Cabrini. This humble Italian woman founded the Missionaries of the Sacred Heart, traveled to the United States to serve fifty thousand Italian immigrants by providing schools and orphanages for their children, and eventually established sixty-seven houses of sisters. Thus, she became the spiritual mother to many.

In the homily of her canonization, Pope Pius XII said, "Undoubtedly she accomplished all this through the faith which was always so vibrant and alive in her heart; through the divine love which burned within her; and finally, through constant prayer by which she was so closely united with God from whom she humbly asked and obtained whatever her human weakness could not obtain."

Mother Cabrini was born in Lombardy, Italy, the youngest of thirteen children, only four of whom survived. Although sickly and weak throughout her childhood, Frances was enamored with stories of missionaries, and dreamed of becoming one herself. At the age of twenty-two, she was turned away from a convent because of her health, so she went to a nearby orphanage to teach. After working for three years with the Sisters of Nazareth, who ran that institution, they allowed her to make her religious vows with them and she was appointed superior of the orphanage.

In 1888, Mother Cabrini received approval to start her own religious order, and was asked by Pope Leo XIII to go to America to care for the many Italian immigrants who had flocked to New York. Upon making the arduous journey in 1889, she was met with a lack of support, a language barrier, and a population discouraged and alienated from its Catholic roots. Nevertheless, she persisted in her call despite the many obstacles, and she began working wherever she could. Her first orphanage began with seven orphans.

Many stories are told about Mother Cabrini's great faith and trust in God, which emanated from a life of prayer. In one story, Mother Cabrini was in need of property for an orphanage in Seattle. As she slept one night, Mother dreamed of a beautiful house that sat upon a big hill. The next day, Mother and two of her sisters were walking when a chauffeur-driven limousine drove by. Mother Cabrini flagged down the limo and asked for a ride back to the convent.

The woman riding in the limo was pleased to assist the sisters, and as they rode along, Mother Cabrini shared with the lady the dream she had the night before. When the party arrived at the convent, the lady told her: "Mother Cabrini, that house you dreamed of is mine. I never thought of parting with it, but if I may be allowed to enter your Holy House for a moment and receive a glass of water in the name of Our Lord, your little orphans shall have their home with my blessing." Later, when asked how she had received such a beautiful piece of property, Mother Cabrini simply said, "I paid for it with three treasures: my love, a dream, and a glass of water in His Name."

Truly, these words of Pope Pius XII aptly describe Mother Frances Xavier Cabrini, who proved that great things are possible for one who is led by the Spirit of God: "Although her constitution was very frail, her spirit was endowed with such singular strength that, knowing the will of God in her regard, she permitted nothing to impede her from accomplishing what seemed beyond her strength." For more information about this wonderful saint, go to www.cabrini.com.

FAITH IN ACTION

Through prayer, Mother Cabrini discovered God's will and received the grace she needed to persevere despite challenges and reversals. How have I seen this in my own life? How can I change my outlook concerning failure or rejection, so that I can see God working His holy will through them?

Woman of Grace

St. Julie Billiart (1751-1816)

From her youth, Saint Julie Billiart lived out the call to spiritual motherhood by bringing the love of Jesus to every circumstance and to everyone. Nothing — not even trial and difficulty — could rob her of her zeal. This poorly educated French farm girl, recognized that every adversity conceals an opportunity to be a woman of grace and witness to the faith.

By age seven, Julie knew her catechism by heart and delighted in sharing it with her companions. Gathering a group of children around her like a mother hen, Julie would instruct them in the faith. Her progress in the spiritual life was so evident that she was permitted to receive her First Communion and Confirmation at the age of nine.

When Julie was sixteen, misfortunes began to overtake the Billiart family. Julie aided her parents by working in the fields with the reapers and riding to market with her father. Her interaction with others both in the fields and in the marketplace so evidently displayed her virtue and piety that she soon was called "the Saint of Cuvilly."

Julie's love and trust in God was severely tested at the age of twenty-two, when her father was shot by an unknown enemy. The shock of the assassination attempt rendered Julie paralyzed in her lower limbs, and she became confined to her bed. Even then, Julie continued to be a spiritual mother to those who came to visit her. She catechized the village children, prepared them for First Communion, and made linens and lace for the altar of her church. But perhaps her greatest influence on souls came from the four to five hours a day she spent in contemplative prayer, leading to a depth of spirituality which continued to grow throughout her life.

During the "Reign of Terror" of the French Revolution, Julie's strong faith caused her to become a target of the Jacobin revolutionaries. She was forced to leave her home and seek refuge in Amiens. There she met Francoise Blin de Bourdon, Viscountess of Gezaincourt. Though the noblewoman was initially put off by Julie's disability, she grew to love and admire Julie's inner beauty. A small group of highborn ladies soon gathered around Julie's couch for instruction, where she taught them how to cultivate a deeper interior life while devoting themselves to acts of charity within the community.

In 1804, Julie along with Francoise founded the Sisters of Notre Dame de Namur, a religious order dedicated to the education of poor girls and the formation of teachers. A few months after the founding, on the Feast of the Sacred Heart, Julie was miraculously healed of her paralysis. She spent the next twelve years until her death working in this new community.

Saint Julie Billiart was canonized by Pope Paul VI on June 22, 1969 for having responded to the call to commit her life to God and to spread the Gospel far and wide. Wherever she went, Saint Julie had imbued hearts and souls with tender affection and true love of God. Despite many hardships, she had been the spiritual mother of many souls.

> *"Oh, how good is the good God!"*
>
> SAINT JULIE BILLIART

FAITH IN ACTION

What gifts do I have that God might want to use in my capacity as a spiritual mother? Have other people mentioned a particular gift or ability of mine that I can use to serve God in this way?

Lesson One

Heralds of the Gospel

Prayer to the Immaculate Heart of Mary

Fount of love, forever flowing,
With a burning ardor glowing,
Make me, Mother, feel like thee;
Let my heart with grace gifted
All on fire, to Christ be lifted,
And by Him accepted be.

ATTRIBUTED TO JACOPONE DA TRODI (13TH C.)

WEEKLY THEME

Fully surrendered as Women of Grace and following in the footsteps of the Blessed Virgin Mary, we are called to "aid humanity in not falling."

WEEKLY GRACE

I pray for the grace to accept my mission as a Woman of Grace and to pattern my life after the Blessed Virgin Mary.

Full of Grace: Read pages 195 - 200 in the text, and then answer the following questions.

1. What two "activities" help women to discover the profound dignity of their position in the kingdom of God? Explain.

2. Name some secondary mediators from the Old Testament, then from the New Testament. Can you name any from our day and time?

3. Explain why the Blessed Virgin Mary is our spiritual mother.

4. What is the significance of the biblical understanding of "home" as it pertains to John 19:25-27? How does this apply to you?

KNOW THE FAITH

Mary Visits Her Children

From the earliest times, the history of the Church is studded with appearances of the Blessed Virgin Mary following her Assumption into heaven. Sometime before his death in AD 270, for example, Our Lady appeared to St. Gregory of Thaumaturge, the "Wonder Worker." She also appeared to St. Athanasius (AD 296-373) and St. John Damascene (AD 676-787?), both Doctors of the Church. Many founders of religious orders were graced by her appearance, and legend has it Our Lady personally selected the site for the Basilica of St. Mary Major in Rome (circa AD 325) through her appearance during a miraculous summer snow. Throughout the ages apparitions of Our Blessed Mother have continued, including many even in our present day and time.

Why does Mary continue to visit her children? As the *Catechism of the Catholic Church* teaches, God revealed Himself fully in His Son, Jesus Christ the Word of God, and there will be no further revelation after Him (#73). Public revelation, therefore, ended with the death of the last apostle. While God's revelation has been completed, "it has not been made completely explicit." As the Catechism says, "...it remains for Christian faith gradually to grasp its full significance over the course of the centuries" (#66).

It is into this latter understanding that apparitions fall. Called *private revelations,* these supernatural appearances add nothing to the deposit of faith but rather help the faithful to live it more fully in a certain period of history (#67). The faithful is under no obligation to believe in an apparition or its message. However, those who approach an apparition with humility of heart and docility of spirit have received great spiritual help and assistance, so long as they give complete assent to the findings and guidance of the Magisterium of the Church with regard to the legitimacy of any purported appearance.

The apparitions of the Blessed Mother are yet another sign of her spiritual maternity. She comes to convert the hearts of her children; to stimulate their faith in the Father's love, mercy and justice; to give the Church hope and courage, zeal and understanding. She comes to nurture her afflicted and suffering children; to warn and encourage them about things to come; to correct them and reprove them when situations and events demand it. In all of these ways, she proves herself a compassionate and loving mother, but also a true handmaid of the Lord, a trusted and faithful daughter of the Most High God.

In all these things, the Blessed Virgin Mary is our mentor who guides us in the way of true spiritual motherhood. As St. Teresa Benedicta of the Cross (Edith Stein) wrote, "Whether she is a mother in the home, or occupies a place in the limelight of public life, or lives behind cloistered walls, [woman] must be handmaid of the Lord everywhere. So had the mother of God been in all circumstances of her life...Were each woman an image of the Mother of God, a Spouse of Christ, an apostle of the divine Heart, then would each fulfill her feminine vocation no matter what conditions she lived in and what worldly activity absorbed her life" (*Ethos on Women's Professions*).

And so the apparitions of the Blessed Mother take on a special and particular significance for women. These appearances are lived lessons in humility, beneficence, and service that allow us to study the various dimensions and attributes of spiritual motherhood. Women of grace learn from the messages themselves, of course; however, Our Lady also instructs us by her very character and demeanor, her qualities and virtues. Mary is a mentor informing us of the way we should go, that we might nurture others to fullness of life in Christ Jesus. We learn what it means to mediate on behalf of the poor and downtrodden, and what it means to suffer for and co-passion with. In short, by looking to Our Lady in her various apparitions, women of grace come to a deeper appreciation of our dignity and vocation, and of the gift of authentic femininity.

1. When did public revelation end? What is the purpose of private revelation?

2. Of the approved and recognized apparitions of the Blessed Mother, which one speaks to your heart the most? How do you see Our Lady's spiritual maternity through it?

3. Read again the words of Edith Stein. Think about the various aspects of your daily life. In what ways can you be a "handmaid of the Lord" in them? Refer to your answer for Number 2. What one quality of Our Lady's spiritual maternity can you emulate in the day-to-day aspects of your life? How does this "make present" the divine Heart?

WORD TO KNOW

Apparition: A supernatural vision or manifestation, corporeal or incorporeal, permitted by God and perceived by the senses. Though some are approved by the Church, these manifestations do not to carry the same weight as articles of faith. The major approved apparitions of the Blessed Virgin Mary include Banneux, Belgium in 1933; Beauraing, Belgium, 1932-1933; Fatima, Portugal in 1917; Guadalupe, Mexico in 1531; Knock, Ireland in 1879; La Salette, France in 1846; Lourdes, France in 1858; Paris, France in 1830. Sacred Scripture testifies to many apparitions (cf. Tobias 3:16-17; Luke 1:11-26; Acts 8:26; Genesis 26:24; Ezekiel 1-3; Daniel 8:15-18; and Acts 9:10).

FOR PONDERING...

Mother of All Humanity

Everyone needs mothering, so Jesus gave us His mother to be our Mother. If we have had wonderful mothers, we have no problem turning to Mary. Unfortunately, all mothers are not like Mary. Some are cold or distant, others manipulating or controlling, others have a problem with alcohol or drugs.

How can we trust Mary's motherly love if we have never experienced it firsthand? The answer is simple. We need to forgive our natural mothers for all the things they may have done — and continue to do — that hurt us, and for all the things they failed to do and continue to fail to do.

A priest giving a women's retreat devoted one of his talks to the importance of going to Mary in prayer. He talked about how natural it is for us to run to our mothers when we have a problem, and how it is just as natural to turn to Mary in prayer. One of the women found the talk upsetting. When she had a problem, she never turned to her mother, because her mother exacerbated every problem she had. How could she turn to Mary as mother when she didn't trust mothers?

Mother's Day was a particular nightmare for this woman. She would dutifully send a gift, but she hated picking out the card. Every card praised mothers for the wonderful things they did for their children, but her mother hadn't been sweet and giving. She felt like a hypocrite sending a card that said her mother had attributes she clearly did not have. When she thought of her mother, all she could remember was the pain, conflict, and anger.

When this un-mothered woman was able to forgive and accept that her mother would never match the greeting card image of motherhood, she realized that she still needed mothering. So she asked Mary to be her true mother.

After a lengthy process of healing, the woman was able to see that her own mother had also never been mothered, and thus didn't know how to mother. When the woman no longer expected her own mother to supply the mothering she needed, their relationship improved. As time passed, their roles were reversed and the daughter was able to give the mother love, tenderness, and real mothering.

DO'L

What is my experience of being mothered? How does this help or hinder my relationship with the Blessed Mother? How did the woman in the above story begin to live out her call to spiritual motherhood? Is there someone in my life that can benefit from the same? Who and how can I help?

____

____

____

IN CLOSING...

"A unique privilege of our Blessed Mother's motherhood, was her ability to give Christ to the world both physically and spiritually. As Christian women we are called to collaborate in the salvation of the world through the vocation of motherhood, whether it is exercised spiritually or physically."

MARIANNE EVANS MOUNT

Dear Lord,
No matter my state or stage in life, I am called to be "mother" by virtue of my feminine personhood. Teach me to exercise this noble vocation in the midst of my life's situations and circumstances. Help me to develop the gifts and attributes so necessary to spiritual motherhood. Following after the example of our Blessed Mother, I desire to bring Your life to the world. May this be accomplished in me, in Your Holy Name. Amen.

Lesson Two

Mary Brings the Word of God to the World

Prayer: O Virgin Immaculate… My Mother

O Virgin Immaculate, Mother of God, My Mother,
from your sublime heights
turn your eyes of pity on me.
Filled with confidence in your goodness
and knowing full well your power,
I beg you to extend to me your assistance
in the journey of life,
which is so full of dangers for my soul.

In order that I may never be a slave of the devil through sin,
but may ever live with my heart humble and pure,
I entrust myself wholly to you.
I consecrate my heart to you forever,
my only desire being to love your divine Son, Jesus.
Mary, none of your devout servants has ever perished;
may I, too, be saved.
Amen.

ST. EPHRAEM OF EDESSA

WEEKLY THEME

Fully surrendered as Women of Grace and following in the footsteps of the Blessed Virgin Mary, we are called to "aid humanity in not falling."

WEEKLY GRACE

I pray for the grace to accept my mission as a Woman of Grace and to pattern my life after the Blessed Virgin Mary.

Full of Grace: Read pages 200 - 206 in the text, and then answer the following questions.

1. Of the three excuses commonly used for not evangelizing, which apply to me? What is the resolution for me?

2. Why is a personal testimony a good way to evangelize? Make a list of the personal stories you can use for your various testimonies. Develop one of them and practice it with a family member or friend.

3. Name three ways that love and consideration are shown when evangelizing.

   a. ____________________

   b. ____________________

   c. ____________________

4. What are two effective means to evangelize loved ones or close friends? Explain each.

   a. ____________________

   b. ____________________

KNOW THE FAITH

Mary Visits Her Children: Our Lady of Fatima

Nine-year-old Lucia dos Santos looked into the angry face of her mother and wondered if this was what the Beautiful Lady meant when she said Lucia would suffer. Little Lucia had never experienced such fury from her mother, nor had her mother ever called her a liar before. Indeed, her heart was deeply saddened. Yet a warm glow filled her whenever she thought about the Lady from Heaven who had visited her and her younger cousins, Jacinta and Francisco.

The three children had been tending their sheep the day before in the Cova da Iria, a portion of the land owned by Antonio dos Santos, Lucia's father. Suddenly, something like lightning flashed in the blue sky and frightened them. The children ran for cover. Another flash, very close, and they ran again. When they stopped, there on top of a small evergreen tree was a large ball of light engulfing a beautiful woman, "a Lady of all white, more brilliant than the sun dispensing light…"

Tenderly, the beautiful woman told the children not to be afraid; she would not hurt them. Lucia assumed the role of spokesperson. "Where do you come from?" she asked.

"I am from heaven," came the Lady's answer.

"And what is it you want of me?" Lucia continued. The lovely Lady told her that she wanted the children to return at the same time on the thirteenth day for the following six months. At the last visit, she would identify herself and tell the children what she wanted. Lucia then asked if she would go to heaven, to which the Woman said, "Yes."

"And Jacinta?" asked Lucia.

"Also," replied the Lady.

"And Francisco?"

"Also," said the Lady, "But he will have to say many rosaries!" Then the Beautiful Lady asked the children this question: "Are you willing to offer yourselves to God and bear all the sufferings He wills to send you, as an act of reparation for the sins by which He is offended, and of supplication for the conversion of sinners?"

Lucia thought for a moment about another heavenly being who had visited her and her cousins. An angel who identified himself as the "Angel of Peace" had appeared to them three times. He had given them Holy Communion and exhorted them to pray and make sacrifices. It seemed as if the Angel of Peace had prepared the children for their response to the Lady's question. Lucia answered for all three of them, "Yes," she said.

"Then you are going to have much to suffer, but the grace of God will be your comfort," the Lady replied.

At that moment, the children were infused with a heavenly light. They felt the presence of God, and offered prayers of adoration. When they were finished, the Lady said, "Say the rosary, to obtain peace for the world, and the end of the war." With that, the beautiful woman rose from the bush and glided away into the sky. That was Sunday, May 13th, 1917, eighteen months before the end of World War I, which at that time had been the bloodiest and most violent war to date.

Lucia continued to suffer the wrath of her mother, Maria Rosa, and her sisters. When the day arrived for the second apparition, several people came to accompany the children to the Cova. Maria Rosa was outraged by the show of support, which made things all the more difficult for Lucia. The entourage arrived at the Cova around 11:00 AM. As the children prayed the rosary, the crowd recited the Litany of Our Lady. Just about noon, the sun dimmed and the tip of the small evergreen tree bent ever so slightly. The Lady had appeared again.

Lucia remained the spokesperson for the group. Our Lady reminded her that she and the children were to come on the same day at the same time the following month. She also asked them to recite five decades of the rosary each day, and she told them they were to learn to read. Lucia asked again if the Lady would take the three of them to heaven. The Lady said that Jacinta and Francisco would go to heaven soon but Lucia would remain on earth for some time to help establish devotion to her Immaculate Heart.

Lucia was sad at the thought of being left alone, but Our Lady said that her Immaculate Heart would be Lucia's refuge. Then Our Lady extended her hands, and great shafts of light poured upon the children. All three of them saw a vision of the Immaculate Heart, and they were filled with indescribable joy and peace.

Following the apparition, the three little shepherds made their way home. Jacinta and Francisco were met with a neutral response, while Lucia received a reception even more hostile than before. The very next morning, Maria Rosa took Lucia to see the parish priest, who warned them that the visions could be coming from a diabolical source. Lucia was frightened and spent the whole month worried that she might be encountering the devil himself. Tormented with fear and beaten down by Maria Rosa's bitter comments, Lucia decided she would not go to the Cova for any more apparitions. However, when Jacinta and Francisco tearfully told her they wouldn't go without her, she changed her mind.

Nearly three thousand people were at the Cova da Iria on July 13th, waiting for the young visionaries to arrive. When the Blessed Mother appeared to the children, she once again asked them to return the following month and reminded them to pray the rosary for peace. And then something remarkable occurred. Shafts of light flowed from Our Lady's hands through the children to the earth below them. Suddenly, the ground seemed to roll back and the three visionaries were staring into the pit of hell. Years later, Lucia wrote of what they saw: "A sea of fire; and plunged in this fire the demons and the souls, as if they were red-hot coals." Our Lady explained to the children:

"You have seen hell where the souls of poor sinners go. To save them, God wishes to establish in the world devotion to my Immaculate Heart. If what I say to you is done, many souls will be saved and there will be peace. The war (World War I) is going to end, but if people do not cease offending God, a worse one will break out during the pontificate of Pius XI. When you see a night illumined by an unknown light, know that this is the great sign given to you by God that He is about to punish the world for its crimes, by means of war, famine and persecutions of the Church and of the Holy Father.

"To prevent this I will come to ask for the Consecration of Russia to my Immaculate Heart and the Communion of Reparation on the First Saturdays. If my requests are heeded, Russia will be converted and there will be peace. If not, she will spread her errors throughout the world, causing wars and persecutions of the Church. The good will be martyred, the Holy Father will have much to suffer, and various nations will be annihilated. In the end, my Immaculate Heart will triumph. The Holy Father will consecrate Russia to me, and she will be converted, and a period of peace will be granted to the world."

This prophetic word was astonishing for a number of reasons. First of all, the Blessed Mother accurately predicted the elevation of Pope Pius XI, who would not become pontiff until 1922. Secondly, at the time of this apparition the Russian Revolution had not occurred; the Bolsheviks would not take over until the following October. Thirdly, as Our

Lady predicted, communism subsequently spread its errors and atheistic philosophy all over the world. Fourthly, another world war followed the first Great War, erupting during the pontificate of Pope Pius XI and ending during the pontificate of Pope Pius XII. That war introduced the atom bomb and caused even more destruction than World War I.

The following month was particularly difficult for the visionaries. The children were besieged by visitors and curiosity seekers daily. In addition, an anticlerical republic had come into power in Portugal, and the local authorities were keen on putting an end to the Fatima piety. Things came to a political head when the government administrator carted the children away under false pretenses on August 13th, the day scheduled for the fourth apparition. The children were threatened with death unless they revealed the secrets Our Lady had entrusted to them. When Francisco said it didn't matter if they were killed since they would go straight to heaven, they were released. Our Lady then appeared to them and once again asked the children to pray and make sacrifices for sinners. She said, "...many souls go to hell because there are none to sacrifice themselves and to pray for them."

Thousands of people greeted the children at the Cova on September 13th. The apparition was very short in duration but the Blessed Mother promised that the children would see the Lord, Our Lady of Sorrows, Our Lady of Mount Carmel, and St. Joseph with the Child Jesus at the next one.

More than 70,000 people gathered at the Cova da Iria on October 13th. It was a rainy and windy day and the parents feared the children would be killed if no miracle took place. Though she still did not believe in the veracity of the apparitions, Maria Rosa accompanied Lucia to the Cova for the child's protection. Umbrellas dotted the landscape as the children knelt to pray. For a reason she does not know, Lucia encouraged the crowd to close them.

When the Blessed Mother appeared, Lucia asked her one last time, "What do you want of me?"

Our Lady responded, "I want to tell you to have them build a chapel here in my honor. I am the Lady of the Rosary. Let them continue to say the rosary every day. The war is going to end, and the soldiers will soon return to their homes." Many people had come to the Cova seeking to be healed. The Blessed Mother assured them that some would receive a healing but others would first need to amend their lives and ask pardon for their sins. She said, "Let them offend Our Lord God no more, for He is already much offended." These would be Our Lady's last words at Fatima. She opened her hands again, and light shot to the sky.

"Look at the sky!" shouted Lucia. The miracle had begun. As the crowd looked up into the sky, the clouds rolled back to reveal the sun. Suddenly, it was a white disc of light, its brilliance shrouded, so that all could gaze upon it. While this was happening, the children saw a tableau in the heavens, with one scene after the other depicting the mysteries of the rosary. They saw the Holy Family with the Christ Child in the arms of St. Joseph, who blessed the crowd three times. Lucia saw Our Lady of Sorrows and then Our Lady of Mount Carmel. The sun began to dance in the sky, twirling and whirling, shooting rainbow-colored rays all over the earth. The crowd and the landscape were bathed in green, then violet, then red as the sun continued its spinning dance. Shouts of praise and worship rose up to the heavens as the crowd delighted in the light show they were seeing.

Then suddenly, the movement of the sun began to change. It plunged toward the earth, falling ever closer to the panic-stricken people. They dropped to their knees to beg God's mercy. Just as the sun seemed about to touch the earth, it began to recede, eventually assuming its normal position in the sky. To the astonishment of every one gathered at the Cova, their rain-drenched clothing as well as everything about them was bone dry. Truly, it was a "Miracle of the Sun." The children were carried home on the shoulders of some strong men, who made certain they would be protected from the crowd.

Soon after the apparitions ended, Maria Rosa and Jacinta's mother sent their girls to school so they could learn to read. Francisco declined the opportunity, knowing that his life would be a short one. He spent most of his time praying at the Church of St. Anthony at Fatima. On April 4th, 1919, he died of bronchial pneumonia. He was almost eleven years old. Jacinta was already sick by the time her brother died. She had developed pleurisy the summer after Francisco's death and she died on February 20, 1920. Lucia stayed at home with her family until she was fourteen years old.

In June 1921, she left to go to a school run by the Sisters of St. Dorothy at Porto. She joined that order in 1925, eventually leaving it to become a cloistered Carmelite in Coimbra. She took the name Sister Mary of the Immaculate Heart.

The apparitions at Fatima were recognized as "worthy of belief" in 1930. The Blessed Mother had given three secrets to the children. Two of them were shared immediately and the third was not to be revealed until 1960 or upon the death of Lucia, whichever came first. Pope John XXIII and Pope Paul VI both read the third secret. Pope John Paul II read it as well following the assassination attempt on his life on May 13th, 1981. He visited Sister Lucia the following year to the day. Afterward, he consecrated the world to the Immaculate Heart of Mary in collegial union with the bishops of the Church. Pope Pius XII had done something similar in 1942.

On June 26, 2000, The Congregation for the Doctrine of the Faith released the third secret in its entirety. The shrine at Fatima, Portugal remains one of the most visited apparition sites in the world with millions of visitors every year. On February 13, 2005, Sister Lucia Marto died at the age of 97. One can only surmise that she is now united with her beloved Jacinta and Francisco, enjoying the company of the Beautiful Lady who had visited them in time so many years ago.

Note: The Third Secret can be read on the Vatican website.

1. How did Our Lady of Fatima seek to bring the world to Jesus Christ and Jesus Christ to the world?

____

____

2. What are the three primary messages Our Lady of Fatima brought to the world? Why are they as vital now as they were in 1917?

   a. ______________________________

   b. ______________________________

   c. ______________________________

3. Consider the final apparition of Our Lady of Fatima. In it, the Holy Family appears. Why do you think this visual message is particularly important for our day and time? In this, how does Our Lady of Fatima show herself to be a spiritual mother?

____

____

WORD TO KNOW

Private Revelation: A revelation supernaturally given to a person for her own benefit or to benefit a larger group. Private revelation never opposes or adds to the public revelation of Sacred Scripture. Private revelation either highlights some truth of Sacred Scripture, or instructs how to live that truth more faithfully. The purpose of private revelation is to convert hearts, increase faith, renew hope, instruct and admonish. Prophetic utterances are sometimes a part of private revelation, as is the case with the apparitions of Our Lady of Fatima.

FOR PONDERING...

Preserving Lives

Some women are timid about bringing God's Word to others. Others — and I am one of these — find it hard to restrain their enthusiasm. After my conversion I wanted to tell everyone about the Lord. Sometimes I came on too strong and turned people off.

I had to learn when to hold back and when to speak through a process of trial and error, with a lot of error. I had to stop talking, start praying, and listen to the Holy Spirit.

Each time I talked to someone, I wondered why that person hadn't accepted Jesus on the spot. Didn't she know that Jesus paid for all her sins, and that all she had to do was ask for forgiveness and forgive others? I was surprised how many people, even those who attended church regularly, hadn't heard this message.

Often however, the problem was that the woman did not want to repent, and let go of her sins. She didn't see her behavior as sinful, but as the source of comfort — like a life preserver in the storm of life. Coming to Jesus would mean relinquishing that life preserver — a false salvation.

If I tried to pry the life preserver from her hands, she would just cling to it even more tightly. However, if I brought her to shore by talking about the hurts and suffering, the rejection and pain that had tossed her into the ocean, there was still hope. And so I talked to her about God, and how He can heal all her hurts and wounds. If she would just forgive those who had hurt her, she could be free.

It is difficult to speak of freedom to one who has never experienced it firsthand. Even so, I begged her to try forgiveness; if she agreed to forgive just one deep wound, she would begin to experience God's love. This would strengthen her to let go of her other false sources of security and to trust in God.

Each soul is different; each needs a special word from God. If we pray, the Holy Spirit will guide us, and the word we speak will go directly to the heart. "Indeed God's word is living and effective, sharper than any two-edged sword. It penetrates and divides soul and spirit, joints and marrow; it judges the reflections and thoughts of the heart. Nothing is concealed from him; all lies bare and exposed to the eyes of him to whom we must render and account" (Hebrews 4:12).

DO'L

What maternal qualities are needed to draw others into a deeper relationship with Jesus Christ? To whom would Jesus send me today to present His Word to them? What would be my best approach?

IN CLOSING...

"Woman's soul is ...fashioned to be a shelter in which other souls may unfold. Both spiritual companionship and spiritual motherliness are not limited to the physical spouse and mother relationships, but they extend to all people with whom woman comes into contact."

ST. TERESA BENEDICTA OF THE CROSS (EDITH STEIN)

Dear Lord,
You have called me, as woman, to be a gift of self-donation to others. Show me how to acquire the virtues of confidentiality, loyalty, true friendship, sincerity, and love. Help me to order my thoughts, words, and deeds to the benefit of others rather than to myself. Give me the grace to be open and welcoming, warm and attentive. May I always see You in those You bring into my life, and to rejoice in that revelation. Help me to reflect Your love to others through spiritual motherliness. Make my heart that shelter in which the hearts of others may unfold. Amen.

Lesson Three

Mary Intercedes for God's Children

Prayer: Antiphon of the Blessed Virgin

Mother benign of our redeeming Lord,
Star of the sea and portal of the skies,
Unto thy fallen people help afford —
Fallen, but striving still anew to rise.
Thou who didst once, while wond'ring worlds adored,
Bear thy Creator, Virgin then as now,
O by thy holy joy at Gabriel's word,
Pity the sinners who before thee bow. Amen.

ALMA REDEMPTORIS MATER,
FROM THE ROMAN BREVIARY

WEEKLY THEME

Fully surrendered as Women of Grace and following in the footsteps of the Blessed Virgin Mary, we are called to "aid humanity in not falling."

WEEKLY GRACE

I pray for the grace to accept my mission as a Woman of Grace and to pattern my life after the Blessed Virgin Mary.

Full of Grace: Read pages 206 - 217 in the text, and then answer the following questions.

1. Describe the three functions of the Queen Mother in the Old Testament. How does the Blessed Mother fulfill each?

   a. __________

   b. __________

   c. __________

2. Explain the role of an intercessor. In what specific ways is God asking you to be an intercessor?

3. Of the five key actions of an effective intercessor, which one do you most need to develop? What one practical strategy can you employ for each?

4. Which of the five key actions is the "hallmark of the effective intercessor?" What makes it so important?

KNOW THE FAITH

Mary Visits Her Children: Our Lady of Lourdes

Perhaps no other appearance of the Blessed Virgin Mary has captured people's hearts and imaginations like those she made to Bernadette Soubirous in Lourdes, France in 1858. Our Lady appeared eighteen times that year to an impoverished, uneducated fourteen-year-old girl who lived with her family in an old jail. Since that time, more than five thousand healings are reported to have taken place in the spot where the Blessed Mother appeared; sixty-four of them the Catholic Church has proclaimed "miraculous."

In most of her appearances to Bernadette, Our Lady was silent. When she did speak, it was to ask for prayers for the conversion of sinners and to identify herself as the "Immaculate Conception." At Lourdes, the Blessed Mother has continued to show herself as a mother who cares for her children's welfare — in this life and in the next.

The remarkable appearances of the Blessed Virgin to Bernadette began on February 11. That Thursday morning, Bernadette along with her sister Toinette and her cousin Jeanne Abadie had gone to the Gave River area to collect firewood for the family's meager noonday meal. The girls crossed the bridge to an area called Massabielle on the Gave banks. Suddenly, Bernadette heard a rustling sound: "I turned my head toward the field by the side of the river but the trees seemed quite still and the noise was evidently not from them. Then I looked up and caught sight of the cave where I saw a Lady wearing a lovely dress with a bright belt. On top of her feet was a pale yellow rose, the same color as her rosary beads."

Surprised by the sight, Bernadette reached for her own rosary tucked away in the pocket of her dress. However, her arm fell like lead to her side, and though she wanted to make the sign of the cross, she could not. The Lady then signed herself with the cross and, as she did, Bernadette was able to do likewise. Silently, the Lady let her beads slip through her fingers while Bernadette prayed the Hail Marys with hers. When the prayer ended, the Lady vanished.

The other girls had not seen the beautiful Lady, and they were curious about what Bernadette had been doing. After they questioned her repeatedly, Bernadette told them about her vision. The girls agreed to keep her secret, but as soon as she entered the house Bernadette's sister told everything. The Soubirous were displeased, and did not believe the account. Francois begged his eldest daughter not to bring shame upon the family, and Louise spanked the girls roundly after forbidding Bernadette to return to the grotto. It was the first of many persecutions Bernadette would endure.

Bernadette continued to feel a strong yearning to go to the grotto, but out of obedience she resisted. On Saturday, she went to confession to seek the advice of a priest about what was happening, a spiritual practice she continued. He asked permission to talk it over with Abbé Peryamale, the pastor of Lourdes. Bernadette agreed. However, by Sunday word about her experience had spread throughout the village and the pressure of the townspeople was too great. Arming Bernadette with holy water to throw at the apparition in case it was from the evil one, Louise permitted her daughter to return to the grotto. Bernadette arrived, the Lady appeared, and when the young girl sprinkled the entire vial of holy water on her, the Lady only smiled and remained silent.

It was during her third apparition that the beautiful Lady finally spoke to Bernadette. Speaking in the local patois, she asked Bernadette, "Would you have the graciousness to come here for fifteen days?" Feeling the flood of interior peace that always accompanied the Lady's visits, Bernadette immediately agreed. Then the Lady told her, "I do not promise to make you happy in this world but in the next."

Large groups of people began to accompany Bernadette each time she visited the apparition site. As the number grew steadily, so did the concern of the local officials. On the evening of February 21st, Bernadette was hauled to the home of Police Commissioner Jacomet, who angrily interrogated and threatened her about her visions. The fourteen-year-old remained calm and answered with kindness. Bernadette referred to the beautiful Lady as *Aquero* — the local word for "That one" — and remained steadfast in her promise to go to the grotto.

On Wednesday, February 23rd, the Lady appeared and spoke once more. "Penitence," she told Bernadette. This was what she wanted from everyone. "Pray to God for the conversion of sinners," she said. The Lady then asked Bernadette to kiss the ground as a penitential sign for others. Bernadette did as she was told and the crowd began to grumble. What was she doing? they wondered. Was she going mad?

The following day their suspicions seemed to be confirmed. Bernadette once again kissed the ground, moved on her knees to one side of the grotto, and began to dig at the dirt with her hands, as though following some directive. Then she lifted the accumulated mud to her lips and began to drink it.

The onlookers were horrified, but Bernadette was not finished. She tore off some pieces of a plant called dorine and began to eat them. The people were dumbfounded, and quite concerned that their little visionary was losing her mind. They didn't know that the Lady had told her, "Go and drink at the fount and wash yourself" and "You will eat of the plant which is there."

After her unusual actions, Bernadette was besieged by questions. "For sinners," was all she said. Even she was uncertain why her *Aquero* had asked her to do such things.

However, all soon began to be clear. By the very next morning, a small pool of water had collected in the spot where Bernadette had dug. On March 1, the first healing miracle at the grotto occurred. Among the hundreds of people who were there that day was Catherine Latapie, a mother of two small children and pregnant with her third. She had fallen two years prior, paralyzing two of her fingers on her right hand.

As soon as Bernadette left the grotto that day, Catherine plunged her right hand into the clear, cold water that was rapidly filling the grotto. Instantly, she felt a warm peace flow through her. When she took her hand out of the water, her fingers were straight and the paralysis had left them. Her excitement stimulated labor, and she begged the Virgin Mary to get her home safely. Four hours later Catherine delivered a baby boy, who eventually became a priest.

Word of Catherine's healing traveled fast. The next day sixteen hundred people were at the grotto for the apparition. This time the Lady had a message. She said to Bernadette, "Go and tell the priests that people must come here in procession and that a chapel [must] be built here." Bernadette carried the message to Abbé Peyramale who insisted that Bernadette ask the Lady to identify herself. Bernadette complied but the Lady only smiled.

On March 4, the apparitions ended as quietly as they had begun.

Though the townspeople were disappointed that no great defining miracle had taken place to end the apparitions, many in the village still believed it was the Blessed Virgin who had come to them. They prayed for further confirmation. On March 25, the Feast of the Annunciation, their prayers were answered.

Bernadette woke early that morning with a great desire to go to the grotto. She knew this feeling well, and beseeched her parents to let her go. By 5:00 AM they gave in to her pleading. Somehow, Bernadette knew that as soon as *Aquero* arrived, she would identify herself. Four times Bernadette requested to know her name, and on the fourth try, the Lady responded. Folding her hands and looking up to heaven, she said simply, "I am the Immaculate Conception."

Bernadette had no knowledge of what this name meant, but after graciously thanking the Lady, she set out at once for the rectory. When Bernadette told Abbé Peyramale the name her *Aquero* had given her, he was stunned. Only four years earlier, in 1854, the Church had promulgated the dogma of the Immaculate Conception: "We define that the Blessed Virgin was preserved from every taint of original sin…from the first moment of her conception." The Abbé knew that the uneducated, poverty-stricken girl that stood before him could not possibly know the meaning of this title. He also knew she could not have heard it anywhere else, except from the Lady who had been appearing to her. The woman who had visited Bernadette was indeed the Blessed Virgin Mary.

The Blessed Mother visited Bernadette two more times, with the final apparition on July 16. Shortly thereafter, Bernadette entered the convent of the Sisters of Nevers and professed her vows on October 15, 1866. A tubercular condition coupled with asthma took its toll on her, and she died at the age of twenty-nine on April 16, 1879. Her body, incorrupt, lies in state to this day in the convent chapel of Nevers. Bernadette was declared a saint on December 8, 1933, seventy-one years after the Church commended devotion to Lourdes as a Marian site.

Today, Lourdes remains one of most renowned shrines of modern times. Its healing waters continue to be a source of hope and consolation. It is also a constant reminder of our Mother in heaven who intercedes on behalf of her children, who cares about their needs, and who seeks to bring them the ultimate healing — conversion to her Son. "Pray for the conversion of sinners," she says. And we can have confidence that she is doing precisely as she instructs.

1. How did Bernadette demonstrate the five key actions of an effective intercessor?

2. What are the maternal characteristics you see in Our Lady of Lourdes? In what ways do you think she helped Bernadette grow in virtue throughout the duration of her appearances? Which interaction of Our Lady with St. Bernadette did you find most endearing and why?

3. In *Marialis Cultus,* Pope Paul VI says this about the Blessed Mother: "The Blessed Virgin's role as Mother leads the People of God to turn with filial confidence to her who is ever ready to listen with a mother's affection and efficacious assistance. Thus the people of God have learned to call on her as the Consoler of the afflicted, the Health of the sick, and the Refuge of sinners, that they may find comfort in tribulation, relief in sickness and liberating strength in guilt. For she, who is free from sin, leads her children to combat sin with energy and resoluteness" (#57). How does Our Lady of Lourdes prove this statement true? What specific attribute of hers stated in this quote can you begin to emulate and how?

WORD TO KNOW

Preservative Redemption: Largely the theological contribution of Blessed Duns Scotus, preservative redemption explains that God, Who exists outside of time, applied the merits of Jesus' redemptive act on Calvary to Mary at the moment of her conception. Thus, she was conceived without the stain of Original Sin. She is the Immaculate Conception. This understanding does not mean that Mary had no need of redemption, but rather Mary received the effects of Jesus' saving act in the form of sanctifying grace the moment she was conceived in the womb of St. Anne.

FOR PONDERING…

The Little Warrior

Few of us would consider St. Therese of Lisieux to be a warrior. However, she was indeed a "prayer warrior," interceding mightily throughout the course of her short life. One story from her autobiography, *The Story of a Soul*, proves that intercession changes the pray-er as well as the one prayed for:

"Formerly one of our nuns managed to irritate me whatever she did or said. The devil was mixed up in it, for it was certainly he who made me see so many disagreeable traits in her. As I did not want to give way to my natural dislike for her, I told myself that charity should not only be a matter of feeling but should show itself in deeds. So I set myself to do for this sister just what I should have done for someone I loved most dearly. Every time I met her, I prayed for her and offered God all her virtues and her merits. I was sure this would greatly delight Jesus…

"I did not remain content with praying a lot for this nun who caused me so much disturbance. I tried to do as many things for her as I could, and whenever I was tempted to speak unpleasantly to her, I made myself give her a pleasant smile and tried to change the subject…

"When I was violently tempted by the devil, if I could slip away without her seeing my inner struggle, I would flee like a soldier deserting the battlefield. And after all this, she asked me one day with a beaming face: 'Sister Therese, will you please tell me what attracts you so much to me? You give me such a charming smile whenever we meet.' Ah, it was Jesus hidden in the depths of her soul who attracted me, Jesus who makes the bitter things sweet."

In what way was St. Therese's intercession efficacious? How did she exhibit the five key actions of an effective intercessor? For whom should I apply these same strategies in my life?

IN CLOSING…

"The maternal woman understands how to alleviate the difficulties of life by her attentiveness and understanding. She is the great conqueror of everyday life. Every day she conquers by making it bearable. Her greatest moment of conquest arrives when it is barely noticed."

JUTTA BURGGRAF

Dear Lord,

Attentiveness and understanding. How I need those blessed qualities Your mother possessed in such abundance. At the wedding feast in Cana, she was attentive to the need of the bride and groom, and made provision even before they were aware of the lack. Quietly and without fanfare or display she served them. Our Lady was attentive to Your every move as she ascended the Via Dolorosa with You. Empathetically, she understood Your pain and suffered with You as she made that fateful climb. Who noticed as she weaved her way through the crowd? Who knew the interior struggle she endured? No one but You, for You are her Lord as well as her Son.

In Your mercy, bestow upon me a rich endowment of attentiveness and understanding, so that I might grow in perfection. Help me to find in Your mother the pattern for my own spiritual maternity. May her lived expression become my interior motivation. In this way, may I conquer every day by making it bearable for others through You. Amen.

Lesson Four

Mary Suffers, Too

WEEKLY THEME

Fully surrendered as Women of Grace and following in the footsteps of the Blessed Virgin Mary, we are called to "aid humanity in not falling."

WEEKLY GRACE

I pray for the grace to accept my mission as a Woman of Grace and to pattern my life after the Blessed Virgin Mary.

Prayer, Our Lord and Our Lady

They warned Our Lady for the Child
That was Our Blessed Lord,
She took Him into the desert wild,
Over the camel's ford.

And a long song She sang to Him
And a short story told:
And She wrapped Him in a woolen cloak
To keep Him from the cold.

But when Our Lord was grown a man
The Rich they dragged Him down,
And they crucified Him in Golgotha,
Out and beyond the Town.

They crucified Him on Calvary,
Upon an April day;
And because He had been her little Son
She followed Him all the way.

Our Lady stood beside the Cross,
A little space apart,
And when She heard Our Lord cry out
A sword went through Her Heart.

They laid Our Lord in a marble tomb,
Dead, in a winding sheet.
But Our Lady stands above the world
With the white Moon at Her feet.

HILAIRE BELLOC

Full of Grace: Read pages 217 – 225 in the text, and then answer the following questions.

1. What is a "co-redeemer?" How does this apply to the Blessed Virgin Mary? How does it apply to all of us?

____

____

2. Why does the cross lie at the center or heart of the Christian experience?

____

____

____

3. What characteristic must mark our participation in the passion of Jesus and why?

____

____

____

4. What four guidelines does St. Therese of Lisieux give us from her autobiography to help us unite our sufferings to Christ?

a. ______________________________

b. ______________________________

c. ______________________________

d. ______________________________

KNOW THE FAITH

Mary Visits Her Children: Our Lady of Akita

In some mystical way, our sufferings yield great benefit for the kingdom of God when they are united to the passion of Christ. In many of her apparitions, Our Lady speaks of this reality. Such is the case of the Blessed Mother's interactions with Sister Agnes Katsuko Sasagawa in 1973.

Sister Agnes belongs to the religious order of the Handmaids of the Eucharist, in Akita, Japan. On June 12, 1973, she went to the chapel alone to pray. As she entered into prayer, a brilliant light began to emanate from the tabernacle. Sister prostrated herself and remained in that position until the light ceased to shine. The experience lasted for more than an hour. The following three days, Sister Agnes was privileged with the same phenomenon as she prayed before the Blessed Sacrament reposed in the tabernacle.

On June 28, Sister Agnes experienced an excruciating supernatural phenomenon: a cross-shaped wound inside her left hand that bled profusely. Though the pain was great, Sister Agnes complained to no one. At 3:00 AM on the morning of July 6, Sister got up to change the bandage covering her wound. An angel appeared, smiled sweetly at her, and spoke. Sister Agnes recorded the angel's words in her journal.

> *"Do not fear… I am the one who is with you and watches over you. Pray with fervor not only because of your sins, but in reparation for those of all men. The world today wounds the most Sacred Heart of Our Lord by its ingratitude and injuries. The wounds of Mary are much deeper and more sorrowful than yours. Let us go to pray together in the chapel."*

When Sister Agnes arrived in the chapel, the angel disappeared. Sister bowed deeply before the altar and turned toward the small statue of Our Lady that was hewn out of a single block of katsura wood. The statue was bathed in a brilliant light.

Sister Agnes wrote, "I prostrated myself on the ground and at the same moment a voice of indescribable beauty struck my totally deaf ears." The statue of the Blessed Mother began to speak:

> *My daughter, my novice, you have obeyed me well in abandoning all to follow me. Is the infirmity of your ears painful? Your deafness will be healed, to be sure. Does the wound in your hand cause you to suffer? Pray in reparation for the sins of men...Do you say well the prayer of the Handmaids of the Eucharist? Then, let us pray it together: "Most Sacred Heart of Jesus, truly present in the Holy Eucharist, I consecrate my body and soul to be entirely one with Your Heart being sacrificed at every instant on all the altars of the world and giving praise to the Father, pleading for the coming of His Kingdom. Please receive this humble offering of myself. Use me as You will for the glory of the Father and the salvation of souls. Most Holy Mother of God, never let me be separated from your Divine Son. Please defend and protect me as your special child. Amen."*

When the prayer was finished, Our Lady instructed Sister Agnes to pray for the pope, the bishops and priests. She also told her to tell Bishop Ito of Akita all that had transpired. This was the first of three messages that Sister Agnes would receive from the Blessed Virgin through her statue in the chapel. Sister Agnes was obedient to Our Lady's instructions.

On the very same day Sister Agnes received her locution from the Blessed Mother, a few of the sisters saw drops of blood issuing from the inside left hand of the same statue. On four separate occasions, blood flowed from the wound in the statue's hand. Though the wound disappeared in September, the statue began to "sweat," especially on the forehead and neck, emitting a sweet fragrance. This continued until October 15.

Supernatural phenomena continued to occur for Sister Agnes. One day, the pain in her left hand was unbearable. She went to the chapel to pray, and once again her guardian angel appeared and instructed Sister Agnes to "Carefully engrave in the depths of your heart the thought of the blood of Mary." The angel then explained about the bleeding statue of the Blessed Mother, "The blood shed by Mary has a profound meaning. [It] was shed to ask your conversion, to ask for peace, in reparation for the ingratitude and the outrages toward the Lord. ... Pray in reparation for all men. Say to your superior that the blood is shed today for the last time. Your pain also ends today. Tell then what has happened today. He will understand immediately. And you, observe his directions."

Sister Agnes obeyed and communicated everything to Bishop Ito. The pain in her hand disappeared completely.

On August 13th, the statue of the Blessed Mother spoke to Sister Agnes for the second time. Again, Our Lady pleaded for prayers. She said, "My daughter...listen to what I have to say. It is very important. You will convey it to your superior. Many men in this world afflict the Lord. I desire souls to console Him, to soften the anger of the Heavenly Father. I wish, with my Son, for souls who will repair by their suffering and their poverty for the sinners and ingrates."

Our Lady then told Sister Agnes about a great chastisement that would fall upon all mankind because of the sin and ingratitude of the world if people do not pray. She said, "With my Son I have intervened so many times to appease the wrath of the Father. I have prevented the coming calamities by offering Him the sufferings of the Son on the Cross, His Precious Blood, and beloved souls who console Him, forming a cohort of victim souls. Prayer, penance and courageous sacrifices can soften the Father's anger." She then expressed the special role that the Handmaids of the Eucharist would fulfill in this regard.

On October 13, Sister Agnes received her last message, a message of warning and encouragement. Our Lady said, "...As I told you, if men do not repent and better themselves, the Father will inflict a terrible punishment on all humanity... The only arms which will remain for you will be the Rosary and the Sign left by My Son. Each day recite the prayers of the Rosary. With the Rosary, pray for the pope, the bishops, and priests. The work of the devil will infiltrate even into the Church...The demon will be especially implacable against souls consecrated to God. The thought of the loss of so many souls is the cause of my sadness... Pray very much the prayers of the Rosary. I alone am able still to save you from these calamities. Those who place their confidence in me will be saved."

Over the course of several years, the statue of Our Lady of Akita shed tears 101 times. On the last day the statue wept, Sister Agnes was again visited by her angel. The angel told her that the figure of 101 is significant. It signifies that sin came into the world by one woman (Eve) and so too did salvation come into the world by a woman (Mary). The zero signifies the eternal God.

Scientific analysis was done on the blood, sweat, and tears emitted by the statue. The Faculty of Forensic Medicine at the University of Akita ruled that the liquids were real human tears, perspiration, and blood. They came from three blood groups — O, B, and AB.

In 1981, a Korean woman was healed of incurable brain cancer while praying before the statue. Her healing was officially confirmed by both the St. Paul Hospital in Seoul and the Archdiocese of Seoul. On May 30, 1982, Sister Agnes' deafness was completely healed. In April 1984, Most. Reverend John Shojiro Ito, Bishop of Akita, declared the events to be of supernatural origin and stated that, "The message of Akita is the message of Fatima." And in June 1988, Joseph Cardinal Ratzinger, prefect of the Congregation for the Doctrine of the Faith, gave definitive judgment on the Akita events, proclaiming that the messages are reliable and worthy of belief.

1. In her messages to Sister Agnes, the Blessed Mother talks about the value of redemptive suffering. How is Our Lady personally involved in this spiritual work? How does Sister Agnes participate? In what ways can you enter into this work of mercy?

2. How is the spiritual motherhood of the Blessed Virgin apparent in her messages to Sister Agnes? In her specific care for Sister Agnes? In what ways can you imitate Our Lady's virtues and maternal charity?

3. Reread the third message of Our Lady to Sister Agnes. Notice that the warning is conditional. What does the Blessed Mother say we can do to avert the calamities that could come as a result of sin? What are you willing to do? How does this fulfill the call to spiritual motherhood?

WORD TO KNOW

Locution: Words of supernatural origin that are heard by the ear or in the imagination. Locutions are also thoughts supernaturally communicated directly to the intellect. The words are clearly understood and convey an assurance of their truth. They penetrate the soul deeply and therefore are retained in the memory for a long time. The validity of all such consolations should be tested to discern their authenticity. Those coming from God leave the soul at peace, lead to on-going conversion, and encourage the soul toward the things of God. Those coming from counterfeit sources do the opposite.

FOR PONDERING...

The Mystery of Suffering

"By her maternal charity, Mary cares for the brethren of her Son, who still journey on earth surrounded by dangers and difficulties, until they are led to their blessed home" (Lumen Gentium, #62).

Catholic women throughout the centuries have endured incredible sufferings with faith and trust, knowing the redemptive value of these trials when they are united to the sufferings of Christ. Beginning with the great saints, an unimaginable number of women knew the efficacy of such self-sacrificing prayer. In this way, they were indeed daughters of the Blessed Virgin, emulating their Mother whose loving and sinless heart beat empathetically while on earth, as it continues to do now in heaven for all of mankind.

I may be the only Catholic in the world who has not always been fond of Michaelangelo's famous Pieta, the statue of Mary holding the lifeless Jesus in her lap. A reproduction in wood happened to be in an alcove of my parish church when I lost my own son. Then I understood. I put my hand into hers and, numb with pain, stared into her eyes. Through that image of the suffering Mother, Our Lady sent healing graces into my heart.

None of us wants to suffer. But since the Fall in the Garden of Eden, we have inherited a sinful world. We are assured of suffering. In the midst of joy and wonder, in the glory and beauty of creation, there lies suffering's great mystery. Christ was not spared, and neither will we be spared — "the servant is not greater than the Master." The mystery of the cross is at the heart of the Christian message. The great saints — all of whom began as ordinary people like you and me — understood that it is not that we suffer, but how we bear that suffering that defines us. Our suffering can refine us, emptying us completely of pride and arrogance and filling us instead with a maternal heart for the suffering of others. Then, our suffering becomes redemptive, and great good can be accomplished for the Kingdom of God through our own blood, sweat, and tears united with those of Christ.

RC

Consider this statement of Pope Paul VI (March 24, 1967): "What would become of a Gospel, of a Christianity without the Cross, without pain, without the sacrifice of pain? It would be ... a Christianity without Redemption...The Lord has saved us with the Cross; with his death. He has given us hope again, the right to life..." Now read 1 Colossians 1:24 and 2 Corinthians 1:4-7. How does the Holy Father's statement coupled with the passages from Sacred Scripture, underscore the value, purpose, and benefit of redemptive suffering?

___

___

___

IN CLOSING...

"We pray, suffer, and labor in ignorance of the consequence of our acts and prayers. God makes them serve His supreme plan; gradually they take effect, winning one soul, then another. They hasten the coming of the Kingdom of God and by the other beings, acts, and desires they give birth to, they will exert an influence that will endure until the end of time."

—ELISABETH LESEUR

Dear Lord,
In this life I may never fully appreciate how You have used my words, my prayers, and my sacrifices to lead others to You. But I know that everything offered to You yields fruit for the Kingdom. Help me to appreciate the mystery of redemptive suffering, the mystical reality of prayer offered on behalf of others, and the transformation possible by uniting all of my daily actions and contradictions to Your Cross.

Holy Mother, pray for me, that I may be a faithful and loving daughter today and always. Amen.

Lesson Five

The Hour Has Come: How Will We Respond?

Prayer from the Chaplet of Divine Mercy

Eternal Father,
I offer You the Body and Blood,
Soul and Divinity of Your dearly Beloved Son,
Our Lord Jesus Christ,
In atonement for my sins and
Those of the whole world.

WEEKLY THEME

Fully surrendered as Women of Grace and following in the footsteps of the Blessed Virgin Mary, we are called to "aid humanity in not falling."

WEEKLY GRACE

I pray for the grace to accept my mission as a Woman of Grace and to pattern my life after the Blessed Virgin Mary.

Full of Grace: Read pages 225 - 227 in the text, and then answer the following questions.

1. Where do we live out our spiritual motherhood?

2. Consider this statement by Pope Pius XII: "...Every Christian woman without exception is under ... a strict obligation of conscience... not to remain aloof. Every woman must go into action, each in her own way, and join in stemming the tides which threaten to engulf the home; in fighting the doctrines which undermine its foundations, in preparing, organizing, and completing its restoration."

   Why do you think the Holy Father says it is a "matter of conscience" for women to "go into action" on behalf of the home and the world? What are some of the "tides" threatening to "engulf the home"? What are the doctrines and ideologies of the day that threaten the home's foundations? In what ways has this study prepared you to go forward to prepare, organize and complete the restoration of the home and the culture?

3. What characteristics mark the soul of woman, according to St. Teresa Benedicta of the Cross (Edith Stein)?

____

____

____

4. Chapter Eight concludes like this: "...God asks each one us the only remaining question: 'My daughters, will you, like Mary your Mother, say yes to your call to bring My life to the world.'" What is your response?

____

____

____

KNOW THE FAITH

Mary Visits Her Children: Our Lady of Guadalupe

Women of Grace® is under the patronage of Our Lady of Guadalupe. The first known apparition to occur in the Americas, Pope John Paul II named Our Lady of Guadalupe "Empress of the Americas." Through her appearances to Juan Diego, the Blessed Mother teaches us much about spiritual motherhood and the call of women in the world.

It was a chilly December morning that ninth day of the month in 1531. Juan Diego was making his way from his home in the village of Tolpetlac to Tlatilolco, the Aztec capital, to continue his studies of the Christian faith. It was not an unusual walk for him, however. Most days he hastily walked this path to attend daily Mass. It was one way he could show his gratitude to God for all of the blessings he had received. Even though he still mourned his deceased wife, Maria Lucia, he remembered with thanksgiving the day they had become Christians just six years before. The baptismal water that poured over them physically was but a symbol of the divine life flowing into their souls. They had been so happy together, their only sadness that they had no children. Juan thought of his uncle, Juan Bernardino, and was thankful that he still had family.

Juan was quickly approaching Tepeyac Hill, one of the main mile-markers on his journey to Tlatilolco. He was always happy to get to this point of the trip — over the hill, across the causeway, and he would be there. Juan's expression darkened, though, as he thought of the pagan rites of human sacrifice that still took place in the capital city, even though his land was now in the hands of Christian leaders. In spite of the Franciscan missionaries' best efforts, conversion was slow among the superstitious and fearful Aztec people, and the bloody human sacrifices continued in an effort to appease their pagan gods. Every year, twenty thousand men, women and children had their beating hearts ripped out in sacrifice to Quetzalcoatl, the "feathered serpent" god. Yes, the beauty of the city certainly did not reflect the horror of the Aztec sacrifices.

The sun was just beginning to break through the night clouds, and as Juan Diego approached the base of the hill, the most melodic of sounds broke the reverie of his thoughts. It was as if the most glorious birds of his country had all come together at once to lift a song to the heavens. When the singing quieted, the music echoed throughout the hillside. Juan shook his head. "What can I be hearing?" he wondered. The singing had a quality all its own, like nothing of this earth yet altogether real.

As he looked east to the top of the hill to find the source of the music, he heard someone calling his name saying, "Juan Diego, Juan Diegito." He climbed the hill in the direction of the voice and found himself facing a beautiful maiden who beckoned him to come closer. Joy flooded his heart as he approached her, and her beauty and splendor all but overcame him. He immediately knew who she was. When the maiden asked him where he was going, he called her, "My Lady, my Queen, my Little Girl."

Then the lovely Lady spoke to him in earnest. "Know for sure my dearest, littlest, and youngest son, that I am the perfect and ever Virgin Holy Mary, Mother of the God of truth … I want very much to have a little house built here for me, in which I will show Him, I will exalt Him, I will make Him manifest. I will give Him to the people in all my personal love, in my compassion, in my help, in my protection: because I am truly your merciful Mother, yours and all the people … who love me, those who seek me, those who trust in me. Here I will hear their weeping, their complaints, and heal all their sorrows…" Our Lady continued to address Juan and entrusted him to bring her request to Bishop Zumarraga of the Franciscans.

Juan Diego left immediately to fulfill Our Lady's request. After waiting all day, however, the bishop dismissed him thinking the little Indian was fabricating the story. Certain he would never return, Bishop Zumarraga told him to come back in a few days. Juan Diego's failure pierced him deeply. Disappointed and dejected, he went directly to the Beautiful Maiden on Tepeyac Hill and suggested to her that she ask someone more suitable to be her emissary. With tender love, Our Lady consoled and encouraged him, and then sent him back to the bishop. This time she instructed him to tell the bishop her name. Juan Diego agreed.

The following day was Sunday. After Mass and religious instruction, Juan Diego hurried to the bishop's residence to again present the Beautiful Maiden's request. This time the bishop interrogated him thoroughly and asked for more evidence to prove the Lady's identity. Confident Our Lady would comply, the faithful little Indian left the bishop's residence and went to tell the Beautiful Maiden. Our Lady received the news with equanimity. "That is fine, my youngest and dearest son; you will return here tomorrow so that you may take the sign he asked for."

But when Juan Diego arrived home, his uncle Juan Bernardino was seriously ill, and it seemed his death was imminent. The uncle begged Juan to go to Tlatilolco the next day to bring a priest to hear his confession. Juan agreed and early the following morning he set off to fulfill his uncle's wish. Concerned he would meet the Beautiful Lady and be detained if he went his usual route, he took a different way around Tepeyak Hill.

However, it is hard to fool one's mother! The Queen of Heaven had been watching for Juan Diego. She came down the hill and stood in front of him, blocking his way. Shamefaced, the little Indian told her why he had tried to avoid her, and promised he would visit the bishop the very next day. After listening intently, the Beautiful Maiden said to Juan, "Am I not your Mother? Are you not under my shadow and protection? Am I not the source of your joy? Are you not in the folds of my mantle, in the crossing of my arms? Do you need anything more? Do not let your uncle's illness worry you, because he will not die now. You may be certain that he is well already."

Relieved, Juan Diego begged Our Lady to provide the sign for the bishop so he could take it to him at once. The Blessed Virgin instructed him to go to the top of the hill. There he would discover beautiful flowers to collect in his tilma and bring to her. Juan knew the top of the hill was no place for flowers to grow. It was December, and the area was craggy and filled with thorns and mesquite bushes. But he obeyed, and when he arrived he found a glorious profusion of Castilian roses blooming there. Gathering as many as his apron could hold, he brought them down to the Virgin who carefully arranged them and instructed him to take them to the bishop.

When Juan arrived at the bishop's residence with his precious cargo, however, he was greeted most unfavorably. The bishop's servants ignored him, then taunted him, and ultimately harassed him to find out what he was guarding. Roughly they poked at him and grabbed at his garment, hoping to sneak a peek at his treasure. Finally they succeeded. When they saw the glorious roses, they were overcome by their scent and beauty and attempted to steal them from Juan Diego. However, when they reached into the tilma, the flowers changed from living blooms to painted ones, seemingly inked onto the apron's fabric. Stunned, they went to the bishop to tell him Juan Diego was waiting to see him.

Upon entering the room, Juan immediately prostrated himself before Bishop Zumarrgara. He then opened his tilma and the precious flowers tumbled to the floor. Immediately the bishop and all of those present fell to their knees. As the flowers cascaded from the apron, the perfect image of the Perfect Virgin, Holy Mary, Mother of God, began to appear on the humble cactus-fiber apron that Juan Diego wore. With supernatural precision and exactness, the likeness of Juan Diego's Beautiful Maiden developed before their very eyes.

As soon as Juan Diego pointed out where the Blessed Lady wanted her chapel to be built, he left to see his sick uncle. Accompanied by a great crowd of people, Juan Diego arrived at Juan Bernardino's house to find him healthy and well. The uncle told his nephew that a Beautiful Maiden appeared to him, healed him, and told him to tell the bishop how he had been cured.

He was also to tell the bishop the proper name for her image. Using his native tongue of Nahuatl, the Virgin said her name was "Coatlaxopeuh" (pronounced "quatlasupe"). Her name sounded remarkably like "Guadalupe," the name of a famous Spanish image of the Blessed Mother. In Nahuatl, however, "coatlaxopeuh" means "The One Who Crushes the Serpent."

Within a few years, the "feather serpent" was indeed crushed. Human sacrifice ceased, and nine million Aztec Indians converted to the Christian faith — the most conversions in the shortest period of time in the history of Christianity. Our Blessed Mother, Star of Evangelization, dressed as an Aztec princess, bore Jesus Christ to the New World and brought the New World to Jesus Christ.

Nearly 500 years later, Juan Diego's famous tilma, with the miraculous image of Our Lady of Guadalupe still clearly visible, hangs in the basilica built to honor her in Mexico City. Replete with religious symbolism, the tilma defies scientific explanation. Some international experts have called it a "living image" because it remains intact though it should have disintegrated centuries ago. For those who believe, Our Lady's image on the tilma of Juan Diego remains an on-going sign of a mother's love for her children.

1. Consider this statement by Jutta Burggraf, a Marian scholar: "Reflecting on the person of Mary sheds light on the specific qualities of a woman, such as her special sense of gratitude and helpfulness; her sense for contemplation; her grasp of the importance of beauty in human life; her capacity for love, support, compassion, warmth, and togetherness. Thus 'it is urgent, as in few other epochs of Church history' to return to Mary. Her being virgin and mother gives the vocation of woman its Christian expression." In the story of Guadalupe, how does the Blessed Mother fulfill the "specific qualities of a woman?" Why do you believe these are necessary for women in the world today? Which of these do you have? Which do you need to acquire?

2. Read Genesis 3:15 in light of Our Lady of Guadalupe. How did she "smite the head of the serpent" in Juan Diego's time? What "serpent heads" do you think she wants to smite in our day and time? How can you aid her?

3. Read again the gentle reproach of Our Lady to Juan Diego, starting with the words: "Am I not your mother?..." As you see these words again, how is Our Lady saying these words to you today? In light of this statement, is there anything to fear as we go forward to "aid humanity in not falling?"

____

____

____

WORD TO KNOW

Relic: The material remains of a saint after her death that are cherished by those with special devotion to that saint, or to encourage increased devotion. There are three classes of relics. A first-class relic is part of the saint's body; a second-class relic is something belonging to the saint, such as a piece of clothing; a third-class relic is something that has been touched by a first-class relic. In Scripture we find evidence of the existence of relics in both the Old Testament (see 2 Kings 2:14, 13:21) and New (see Acts 19:12). In 787 the Second Council of Nicea anathematized those who reject relics, and declared that no church should be consecrated without them.

FOR PONDERING...

In the Army of Holy Women

We are God's army, Women of Grace! Chosen in Him before the foundation of the world, we are to take the Gospel message to the whole world. God did not intend for us to function as isolated individuals. He intended for us to function as His family, His army. He wants us to pray for one another, to encourage and strengthen one another, to raise up a generation of holy offspring in His Name.

How do we accomplish this lofty goal? — By imitating the one who is indeed the woman of grace, our Blessed Mother. All through my Christian life, I have sought out godly role models to follow. I knew that in following their example I would become more like the Christ I love. The apostle Paul said to his disciples, "Follow me as I follow Christ." But there is no quicker, safer, surer route to Christ-likeness than to follow the one who was most like her Son.

In my Protestant years, I feared that devotion to Mary would rob Christ of the devotion rightfully due Him. Now I know that it is impossible to love her too much, for the more we love Mary, the more we will love Christ. She does not reserve the honor we give her for herself, but uses it to lead us into a deep, loving, holy union with her Son. She's a Jewish mother after all! Do you know a Jewish mother who doesn't "want you should know her Son"?

Listen to the words of Bishop Sheen:

"As our love does not start with Mary, so neither does it stop with Mary. Mary is a window through which our humanity first catches a glimpse of divinity on earth. Or perhaps she is more like a magnifying glass that intensifies our love of her Son and makes our prayers more bright and burning.

"God, who made the sun, also made the moon. The moon does not take away from the brilliance of the sun. All its light is reflected from the sun. The moon would be only a burnt-out cinder floating in the immensity of space, were it not for the sun. The Blessed Mother reflects her Divine Son; without Him, she is nothing. With Him, she is the Mother of men.

"On dark nights we are grateful for the moon; when we see it shining, we know there must be a sun. So in this dark night of the world, when men turn their backs on Him who is the light of the world, we look to Mary to guide their feet while we await the sunrise."

And so, dear women of grace, in imitation of Mary we too can guide the feet of those entrusted to our care and the feet of those who in some way cross our paths every day. Remember the letters, WWJD — "What would Jesus do?" We could do no better than to ask WWMD — "What would Mary do?"

She knows and loves her Son more perfectly than any of us do or can, and all of us can learn so much just by following her example. Here's a sample of what Our Lord asked of our Blessed Mother, and what can become of us as her handmaids:

> [Mary] was not asked to become great, but to surrender her littleness to the Infinite Love,
> and as a result to become the Mother of Christ.
> She was not asked to do anything herself, but to let something be done to her.
> She was not asked to renounce anything, but to receive an incredible gift.
> She was not asked to lead a special kind of life… God asked for her ordinary life
> — all of it, daily — even as He asks for ours.
> Our Lady said yes for us all.
> But we each must echo her yes, which like Our Lady's surrender
> Must be a complete and absolute trust, without condition, without reservation.
> We shall not be asked to do more than the Mother of God.
> We shall not be asked to become extraordinary or to offer great, heroic sacrifices.
> What we shall be asked to give is our flesh and blood, our daily life and thoughts
> Our service to one another, our affections and our loves,
> Our words, our intellect, our waking, working, and sleeping,
> Our ordinary human joys and sorrows, give them all to God.
> To surrender all that we are, as we are, to the Spirit of love
> That our lives may bear Christ to the world.

Are you ready to say "yes," dear woman of grace? I hope so. The world needs you.

RM

Consider the call of the handmaid. To what extent are you willing to embrace it? What one grace do you believe God is giving you today to embrace it more fully.

IN CLOSING...

"Yes, Christian women, the future of civil society and of the ecclesial community expects much of your sensitivity and of your capacity for understanding, of your sweetness and of your perseverance, of your generosity and of your humility. These virtues — so well in accord with feminine psychology and magnificently developed in the Virgin Mary — are also the fruits of the Holy Spirit. This Holy Spirit will guide you..."

POPE PAUL VI

Dear Lord,
I pray for the grace to follow in the footsteps of Our Blessed Mother. Help me to imitate her in all things — to test my thoughts, words, and deeds against her example of perfect docility to the will of the Father. As she birthed Jesus Christ and brought salvation to the world, may I birth Him spiritually in the lives of others. In this way I will live out my call of spiritual motherhood and do much to "aid humanity in not falling." I commend myself to the guidance of the Holy Spirit. May I never stray from the narrow road that leads to eternal life. Amen.

Appendix 1: A Closing Prayer

A Daughter's Prayer

Dear Lord,

Throughout this study You have shown me so much about what it means to be a woman. You have shown me that my essential mission is to bring others to spiritual life, to nurture them in their relationship with You, to help them grow strong in the Faith and in Your life. This is accomplished by my call to spiritual motherhood, a call You have ordained for me from all eternity, and a call accomplished through the gift of authentic femininity.

You have shown me that women, impregnated by a spirit of the Gospel, can change the course of the world and the destiny of mankind; and, You have shown me that to be impregnated with You, I must seek a holy life steeped in prayer, the sacraments, renunciation of vices, and growth in virtue.

You have shown me that now is the time for me to step into the fullness of my womanhood, and You encouraged me to do so with fortitude, commitment, and conviction. You have shown me that at this moment, the world desperately needs my gift of spiritual motherhood, and that my witness to the faith will aid humanity in not falling. And, You have strengthened me to persevere in times of tribulation and stress, trial and misunderstanding, confusion and contradiction.

Lord, to strengthen me in my womanhood and gift of authentic femininity, You have given me the Blessed Virgin Mary as my model. Inspired by her act of total self-donation, I pray for the gift of receptivity, the gift of trust, and the gift of surrender. I pray for an open heart, a fertile soul, and a spirit pregnant with Your divine life. May she make intercession for me as I seek to be a woman full of grace in today's culture. And, may I one day stand with her in Your heavenly kingdom, a daughter who continues to bring Your life to the world. Amen

TAKEN FROM GRACE-FILLED MOMENTS
BY JOHNNETTE S. BENKOVIC

Prayer of Consecration to
Our Lady of Guadalupe

Prayed by Johnnette S. Benkovic and participants at the first regional Women of Grace® Conference at the Shrine of Our Lady of Czestochowa

Lord Jesus Christ, Savior and Redeemer;
Incarnate Wisdom, Your humble
submission unto death on the cross revealed the power and the love of the Father.
Your resurrection revealed the presence and action of the Holy Spirit.
You have ransomed us from death and the power of evil
and purchased us at the price of Your blood.
At the hour of Your death, You gave to us the Blessed Virgin Mary and willed her to be
the Mother of the Church, the mother of us all.
In 1531, You sent her to the Americas to be the means through which conversion and reconciliation would
liberate not only the people of Mexico,
but all the people of the Western Hemisphere.
Our Lady of Guadalupe is Patroness of the Americas and therefore
Patroness of our country.

Before this blessed Missionary Image of Our Lady of Guadalupe,
which signifies her presence among us, I do formally consecrate *Women of Grace®*,
its mission, and its outreach to the Immaculate Heart of Our Lady of Guadalupe.
I humbly request the fruit of this consecration be conversion, healing,
reconciliation and salvation.
I further petition Our Lady of Guadalupe to instill
in the hearts of her daughters an ever deepening understanding
and appreciation of the feminine genius;
and I ask that through her motherly influence and maternal intercession,
Our Lady of Guadalupe would lead her daughters to
the Sacred Heart of her Son, Jesus Christ.

Hear my prayer, Lord Jesus, through the powerful love of the
Immaculate Heart of Our Lady of Guadalupe. I make this consecration
with thanksgiving and trust, and for the spiritual welfare of
women everywhere, especially those who are Women of Grace®.
May this consecration deepen the virtues of faith, hope and charity.
May it bring an awesome reverence for the gift of life, physical and spiritual life,
and for Your Real Presence enthroned in the Eucharist.
May it help us to bear witness to the Gospel and to live the teachings of the Catholic Church. And finally, may this consecration help to bring us all to the joy of Your kingdom where You live and reign with the Father and Holy Spirit;
One God forever and ever. Amen.

Appendix 2:

Women of Grace® Theme Song

We are Women of Grace
'Round the throne of the Lord most high;
And we lift up our praise
From the depths of our souls, hear our cry

Oh Lamb of God,
It is our one desire
To see Your Holy Face,
To be Women of Grace.

We'll shout with joy from the mountain top,
As we enter Your courts with praise;
All that we do, Lord;
We offer to You, Lord;
Hear us as we pray.

Appendix 3: Bibliography

Adams, Michael, Translation and typography, *The Navarre Bible*, Dublin, Ireland, Four Courts Press, 1988.

Attwater, Donald, *A Catholic Dictionary*, Rockford, IL, TAN Books and Publishers, 1997.

Baars, Conrad W., M.D., *Feeling and Healing Your Emotions*, Gainesville, FL, Bridge-Logos, 2003, Reprinted and Updated.

Ball, Ann, *Encyclopedia of Catholic Devotions and Practices*, Huntington, IN, OurSunday Visitor, 2003.

Benkovic, Johnnette S., *Experience Grace in Abundance: Ten Strategies for Your Spiritual Life*, Huntington, IN, Our Sunday Visitor, 2003.

Benkovic, Johnnette S., *Full of Grace: Women and the Abundant Life*, Cincinnati, OH,St. Anthony Messenger Press, 2004, Revised.

Benkovic, Johnnette S., *Grace-Filled Moments*, Huntington, IN, Our Sunday Visitor, 2001.

Broderick, Robert C., *The Catholic Encyclopedia*, New York, NY, Thomas NelsonPublishers, 1975.

Bunson, Matthew, D. Min., *OSV's Encyclopedia of Catholic History Revised*, Huntington, IN, 2004.

Chervin, Ronda De Sola, Ph.D., *Prayers of the Women Mystics*, Ann Arbor, MI, ServantPublications, 1992.

Chervin, Ronda De Sola, Ph. D., *Treasury of Women Saints*, Ann Arbor, MI, Servant Publications, 1991.

Chiffolo, Anthony, F., *100 Names of Mary: Stories and Prayers*, Cincinnati, OH, St.Anthony Messenger Press, 2001.

de Souza, Raymond J., *John Paul II and the Problem of Consumerism*, "Religion & Liturgy," September and October, 1999. Vol. 9, Number 5.

Dubruiel, Michael, *The How-To Book of the Catholic Mass*, Huntington, IN, Our SundayVisitor, 2002.

Fernandez, Aurelio and James Socias, *Our Moral Life in Christ*, Scepter Publishers, Inc., 1997.

Flannery, Austin P., Editor, *Documents of Vatican II*, Grand Rapids, MI, William B.Eerdmans Publishing, Co., 1975.

Franciscus, Rev. Pius, O.F.M., Cap., *Mother Love: A Prayer Book for Christian Wives and Mothers*, Pittsburgh, PA, Archconfraternity of Christian Mothers, 1979.

Ghezzi, Bert, *Voices of the Saints: A Year of Readings*, New York, NY, Doubleday, 2000.

Hunt, Robert Dr., "Behold I Make All Things New!" Annual Conference Sermon, 1999.

Johnson, Francis W., *The Voice of the Saints*, Rockford, IL, TAN Books and Publishers,1986.

Kilmer, Joyce, Editor, *Joyce Kilmer's Anthology of Catholic Poets*, New York, NY, Liveright Publishing Corporation, 1939.

Leseur, Elisabeth, *My Spirit Rejoices*, Manchester, NH, Sophia Institute Press, 1996.

Moll, Helmut, Editor, *The Church and Women: A Compendium*, San Francisco, CA, Ignatius Press, 1988.

O'Connor, John Cardinal, "Dorothy Day's Sainthood Cause Begins," www.ny-archdiocese.org.

Odell, Catherine M., *Those Who Saw Her: The Apparitions of Mary*, Huntington, IN, Our Sunday Visitor, 1986.

Pope Pius XII, Selected and Arranged by The Monks of Solesmes, *The Woman in the Modern World*, Boston, MA, Daughters of St. Paul, 1959.

Randall, Beth, "Illuminating Lives: Dorothy Day," 1996, www.mcs.drexel.edu.

Romero, Father Mario P. *Unabridged Christianity*, Goleta, CA, Queenship Publishing, 1999.

Smith, Janet, PH.D., "Humanae Vitae: A Generation Later," 2000, www.goodmorals.org.

Stein, Edith, Ph.D., *The Collected Works of Edith Stein, Vol. II, "Essays on Woman,"*Translated by Freda Mary Oben, Ph.D., Washington, D.C., ICS Publications, 1987.

Stravinskas, Rev. Peter M.J., Ph.D., S.T.L., Editor, *Our Sunday Visitor's Catholic Encylcopedia*, Huntington, IN, Our Sunday Visitor, 1991.

Therese of Lisieux, *The Autobiography of St. Therese of Lisieux: The Story of A Soul*, Translated by John Beevers, Garden City, NY, Image Books, Doubleday, 1957.

Therese of Lisieux, *The Prayers of Saint Therese of Lisieux*, Translated by AletheiaKane, O.C.D., Washington, D.C., ICS Publications, 1997.

Walsh, Thomas, Ph.D., *The Catholic Anthology*, New York, NY, The MacMillan Company, 1927.

Weiser, Francis X., S.J., *Handbook of Christian Feasts and Customs*, New York, NY, Harcourt, Brace and Company, 1958.

CHURCH DOCUMENTS

As the Third Millennium Draws Near (Tertio Millennio Adveniente), Pope John Paul II, November 10, 1994.

Catechism of the Catholic Church, Second Edition, United States Catholic Conference,Inc. (Washington, D.C.) – Libreria Editrice Vatican (Vatican City, Rome, Italy),1994,1997.

Constitution on the Sacred Liturgy (Sacrosanctum Concilium), Pope Paul VI, December 4, 1963.

Decree on the Apostolate of the Laity (Apostolicam Actuositatem), Documents of the *Second Vatican Council*, November 18, 1965.

Dogmatic Constitution on the Church (Lumen Gentium), Documents of the SecondVatican Council, November 18, 1965.

Closing Speeches Vatican Council II, "To Women," read by Leon Cardinal Duval of Algiers, Algeria, assisted by Julius Cardinal Doepfner of Munich, Germany, andRaul Cardinal Silva of Santiago, Chile, December 8, 1965, printed by the Daughters of St. Paul, Boston, MA.

For the Right Ordering and Development of Devotion to the Blessed Virgin Mary (Marialis Cultus), Pope Paul VI, February 2, 1974.

Letter to the Bishops of the Catholic Church on the Collaboration of Men and Women in the Church and in the World, Joseph Cardinal Ratzinger, May 31, 2004.

Letter to Women, Pope John Paul II, June 29, 1995.

Mother of the Redeemer (Redemptoris Mater), Pope John Paul II, March 25, 1987.

On Evangelization in the Modern World (Evangelii Nuntiandi), Pope Paul VI, December 8, 1975.

On Human Life (Humanae Vitae), Pope Paul VI, July 25, 1968.

On Social Concerns (Sollicitudo Rei Socialis), Pope John Paul II, December 30, 1987.

On the Dignity and Vocation of Women (Mulieris Dignitatem), Pope John Paul II, August 15, 1988.

On the Eucharist in its Relationship to the Church (Ecclesia de Eucharistia), Pope John Paul II, April 17, 2003.

On the Most Holy Rosary (Rosarium Virginis Mariae), Pope John Paul II, October 16,2002.

On the Vocation and the Mission of the Lay Faithful (Christifidelis Laici), Pope JohnPaul II, December 30, 1988.

Stay With Us Lord (Mane Nobiscum Domine), Pope John Paul II, October 7, 2004.

The Consecrated Life (Vita Consecrata), Pope John Paul II, March 25, 1996.

WEBSITES

Acton Institute, www.acton.org

Archdiocese of New York, www.ny-archdiocese.org

Apparitions of Jesus and Mary, www.apparitions.org

Catholic Apologetics of America, http://catholicapologeticsofamerica.blogspot.com

Catholic Information Network, www.cin.org

Catholic Online – Saints and Angels, www.catholic.org

Daughters of St. Paul, www.daughtersofstpaul.com

Drexel University, www.mcs.drexel.edu

Eternal Word Television Network, www.ewtn.com

Fatima, Portugal, "Our Lady of Fatima," http://198.62.75.1/www1/apparitions/http:/pr00011.htm

Federation of St. Gertrude, www.federationofstgertrude.org

Good Morals, www/goodmorals.org

Melkite Greek Catholic Church, Eparchy of Newton, www.melkite.org

New Advent, www.newadvent.org

Patron Saints Index, www.catholic-forum.com

Saint Frances Cabrini School, www.cabrini.com

St. Elizabeth of Portugal, http://www.loc.gov/rr/Hispanic

Our Lady of Guadalupe Patroness of the Americas, www.sancta.org

The Catholic Worker Movement, www.catholicworker.org

The Jesus King of All Nations Devotion and The Missionary Image of Our Lady of Guadalupe, www.ourladyofguadalupe.org

The Teresian Carmel, www.karmel,at/eng/teresa.htm

True Catholic, www.marypages.com

Mission To Empty Purgatory, www.mtep.com

Lynn Cooper Music

Contemporary Catholic Singer/Songwriter

Father of Us All: (1995) Simple by design and geared towards children.

On His Wings: (1997) Inspirational & healing, includes Lynn's most known song; *Ten Thousand Angles.*

Comfort From a Manger: (1998) Filled with traditional Christmas songs and songs written by Lynn, herself. Includes *Ave Maria.*

Reign Dance: (2000) Made for the Jubilee year of our Lord. This is a very upbeat and contemporary music collection.

To You Alone: (2002) Lynn's personal devotional songs. Includes the theme song for Women of Grace™.

To You Alone the Devotional: (2002) Read the stories behind the songs of the album of the same title. This devotional has scripture to study as well as a prayer after each song

Songs From the Rocking Chair: (2003) Three songs on Adoption and Pro-life. Featured on *Living His Life Abundantly* with Johnnette Benkovic. Lynn tells her story of adoption on this album. Each song is seen through the eyes of all involved, the Adoptive Parent, Birth Parent and a thank you song by the Child.

The Praise Goes On: (2004) Very upbeat, Praise and Worship music that we all know and have grown to Love. These are the songs the women at the Women of Grace Conferences are sure to be singing.

www.LynnCooperMusic.com

Praise & Worship Leader for Women of Grace™

Theme Song Writer for Women of Grace® * As seen on EWTN and Boston Catholic TV * Featured performer for WYD 2002

For music orders or booking information:
P.O. Box 231 * Pella, IA 50219 * 641.628.1308
www.LynnCooperMusic.com

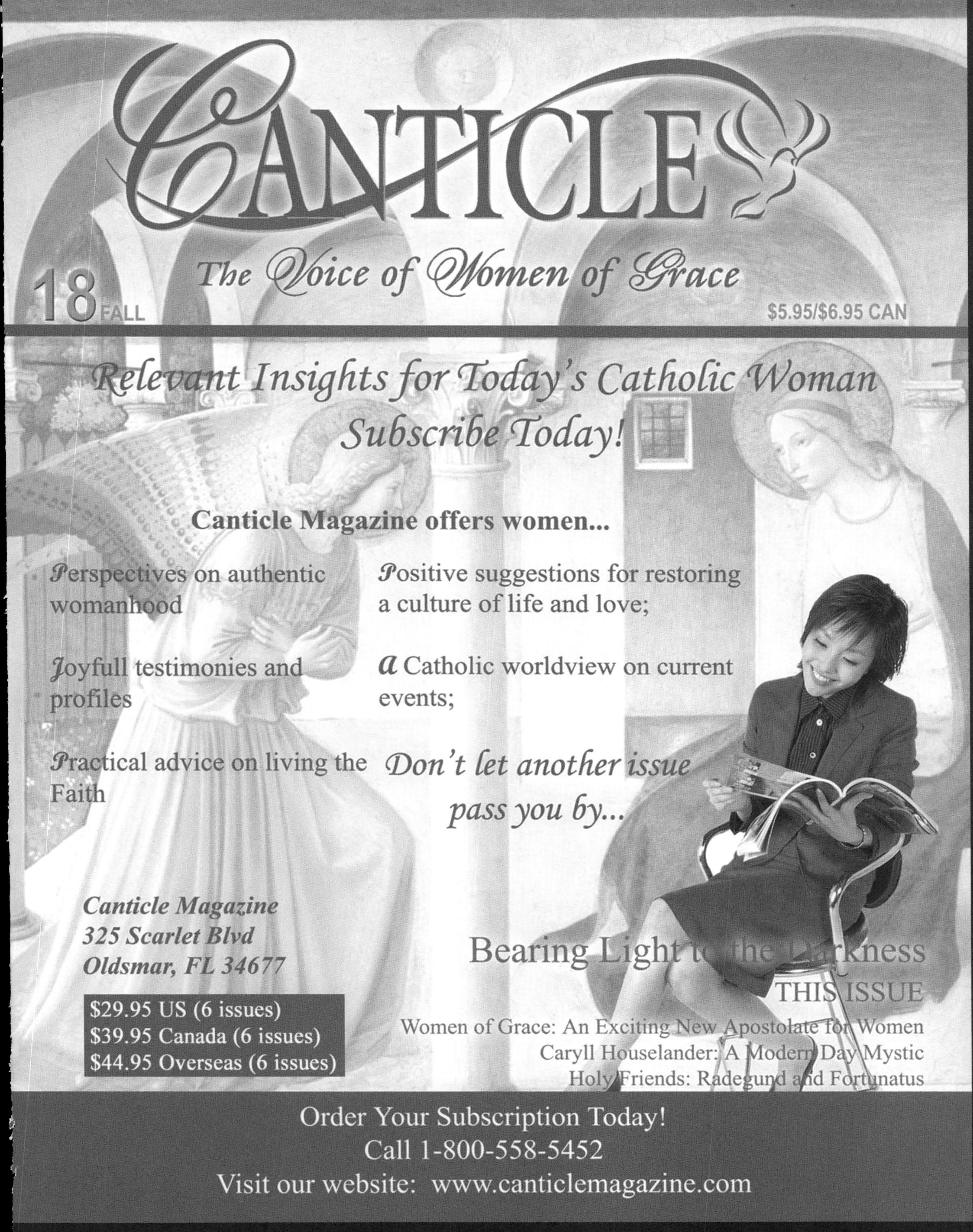
CANTICLE
The Voice of Women of Grace
18 FALL
$5.95/$6.95 CAN
Relevant Insights for Today's Catholic Woman
Subscribe Today!
Canticle Magazine offers women...
Perspectives on authentic womanhood
Joyfull testimonies and profiles
Practical advice on living the Faith
Positive suggestions for restoring a culture of life and love;
A Catholic worldview on current events;
Don't let another issue pass you by...
Canticle Magazine
325 Scarlet Blvd
Oldsmar, FL 34677
$29.95 US (6 issues)
$39.95 Canada (6 issues)
$44.95 Overseas (6 issues)
Bearing Light to the Darkness
THIS ISSUE
Women of Grace: An Exciting New Apostolate for Women
Caryll Houselander: A Modern Day Mystic
Holy Friends: Radegund and Fortunatus
Order Your Subscription Today!
Call 1-800-558-5452
Visit our website: www.canticlemagazine.com